An Introduction to

Differential *and* Integral Calculus

An Introduction to
Differential *and* Integral Calculus

Brian K. Saltzer

The McGraw-Hill Companies, Inc.
Primis Custom Publishing

New York St. Louis San Francisco Auckland Bogotá
Caracas Lisbon London Madrid Mexico Milan Montreal
New Delhi Paris San Juan Singapore Sydney Tokyo Toronto

McGraw-Hill Higher Education

A Division of The McGraw-Hill Companies

An Introduction to Differential and Integral Calculus

McGraw-Hill's Primis Custom Publishing consists of products that are produced from camera-ready copy. Peer review, class testing, and accuracy are primarily the responsibility of the author(s).

1 2 3 4 5 6 7 8 9 0   QPD   QPD   0 9 8 7 6 5 4 3 2 1 0

ISBN 0-07-238368-2

Editor: Shirley Grall
Production Editor: Carrie Braun
Cover Design: Maggie Lytle
Printer/Binder: Quebecor World

TABLE OF CONTENTS

This book is dedicated to my parents.
Without your unbelievable amount of love and support I would not be where I am today.

Preface

My intention in writing this book was to write a calculus book that a beginning technical calculus student could read on his/her own. Unfortunately, when most students are presented with calculus for the first time, they are so buried in mathematical formalism that the techniques and applications elude them.

I have attempted to write a book that is as "user-friendly" as possible. At every stage possible, I have tried to write out the actual sentences that a student would hear in an entry-level lecture on the material. The exercises are also organized in a different fashion than most other textbooks. The solutions to the exercises are immediately following each set of exercises, and have been written out step-by-step.

In a break with mathematical tradition, I have purposely not "simplified" the solutions. For many years I have watched my students' frustration with this particular point. They execute an algorithm to find the derivative, integral, etc. and then try for twenty minutes to see whether or not their answer is equivalent to the "simplified" one in the back of the book. The solutions in this book have been left in their larger, less elegant form specifically so that a student can see whether he/she correctly executed the algorithm.

The material is presented in a manner as simplified as possible and I make no claim of addressing the deeper mathematical rigor. I am of the opinion that the deeper insights in any area of mathematics come with experience and not from the first presentation. It is only after a student has some working knowledge of the methods and procedures that are indigenous to that area of mathematics that the deeper, subtler connections become apparent.

My wish is that this book will show at least one beginning student that calculus is not as frightening as he/she might have believed.

BKS

Introduction

When Isaac Newton first developed the calculus, he did so to solve problems in the real world. Somewhere this has gotten lost. It is an unfortunate fact that, for most students, the first time they are exposed to calculus it is taught as a pure mathematics course. It is only after they progress further into their respective disciplines that they begin to see the extensive set of real world situations to which the calculus can be applied. This book is an effort to redress a portion of this unfortunate situation.

The entire focus of this book is to get the student to the point where he/she can apply the concepts of differentiation and integration as quickly as possible. I make no claim as to the intense rigor of the topic. There are already an unbelievable number of texts in print that approach the topic with full rigor. This book is meant for the student that wishes an entry-level approach to differential and integral calculus without most of the intense analysis.

In a "standard" calculus textbook, a great deal of time is spent on, for example, the concept of the limit of a function. Limits are taken from the right, from the left, etc. and the student spends a substantial amount of time learning how to calculate the limits of more and more pathological functions. This is not the approach that has been used here. The sole reason, from a calculus standpoint, that a student learns about limits is to eventually define the concept of a derivative and the concept of an integral. Once a student has grasped the basic notion of a limit, it is time to move to the next concept.

In addition to burying the unsuspecting student in a sea of mathematical rigor, many "beginning" calculus texts make it very difficult for the student to know whether or not they have actually grasped a concept. The answers in the back of the book, or even immediately adjacent to the sample problem, have been "simplified" to the point that they are almost unrecognizable. The students were presented with an algorithm to solve a certain type of problem, and they followed it. Unfortunately, now they must do fifteen more minutes of algebra to see whether their answer is equivalent to the one in the back of the text. This is not done here! The answers to those problems that are to be solved with a step-by-step algorithm have been left in their rather ungainly form so that the student can, term-by-term, check to see if he/she has done the problem correctly.

The book begins by reviewing the basic ideas of plotting points and graphing. The concept of the slope of a line is then discussed in great detail providing a platform from which to introduce the derivative of a function. After the geometric motivation of the derivative, a step-by-step algorithm is presented for calculating the derivative of a function. Because the focus of the book is to get students to the point where they can differentiate and integrate as quickly as possible, shortcuts for finding the derivatives of functions are immediately introduced following the rather lengthy algorithm. From this point, the book follows the standard topical route found in most calculus texts in the chapters on derivatives.

The book then proceeds to the second portion of calculus, integration. The integral of a function is motivated from a very intuitive standpoint. Integration is first introduced as the area under a curve between definite limits. After the intuitive introduction, techniques are discussed for actually calculating integrals.

At the end of each section of the book, exercises are given with solutions. For the majority of the problems in the text, step-by-step solutions have been included immediately following the problems. For beginning mathematics students, there are few things more frustrating than not understanding how the author jumped from one step to another when solving a problem. A great deal of effort has been put into writing out the details involved in the solution of many of the problems. Those sections that include full, detailed solutions have been identified in the text, in contrast with those sections simply labeled as "Answers".

After having said all this, let's begin!

CHAPTER 1

PRELIMINARIES

<u>Points, Lines, and Slopes</u>

Let's start with a set of coordinate axes. We will call the horizontal axis the x-axis and the vertical axis the y-axis:

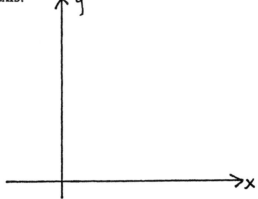

To place a point on our graph we must know how far out the x-axis to go and how far up the y-axis to go. For example, if we move 2 units out the x-axis and 3 units up the y-axis, we arrive at the point (2,3). Remember that coordinates are always expressed with the x-coordinate placed first and the y-coordinate placed second. Plotting the point (2,3):

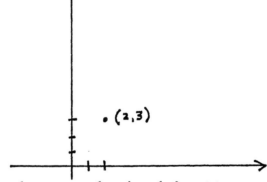

Now that we remember how to graph points, let's put two generic points on our graph. We'll call the coordinates of point 1: (x_1, y_1) and call the coordinates of point 2: (x_2, y_2):

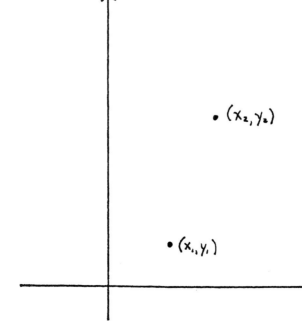

These two points allow us to use a property from basic geometry:

Two points completely define the straight line that is drawn through them.

What this means, in a little less formal language, is that there is only one **unique** straight line that can be drawn through both points:

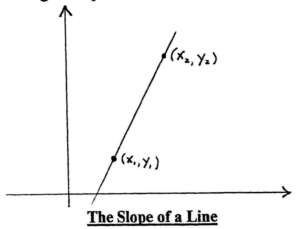

The Slope of a Line

Unfortunately, when most students learn how to calculate the slope of a line for the first time, it is just one of many topics covered in a beginning algebra course.

The concept of slope is the heart of differential calculus

Because of this, we want to spend a fair amount of time learning how to calculate the slope of a line and, more importantly for our purposes, learning how to interpret what the slope means. We will address these topics separately.

Calculating the Slope of a Line

Let's look again at our graph with the two points and the line:

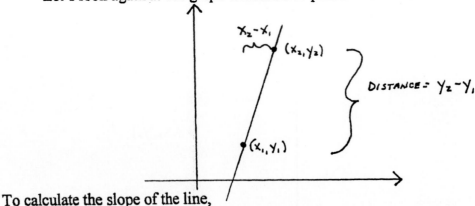

To calculate the slope of the line,

take the difference in the y-coordinates and divide by the difference in the x-coordinates.

If we write this out using the coordinates of our two generic points:

$$slope = \frac{y_2 - y_1}{x_2 - x_1}$$

Let's take our slope equation and calculate the slopes of two different lines.

Example #1

Point 1 = (1,2)
Point 2 = (3,5)

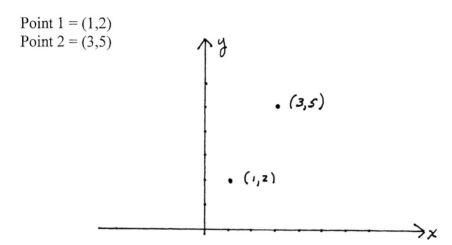

If we now draw the line determined by our two points:

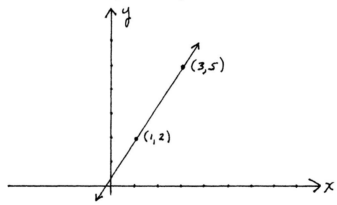

Inserting our two sets of coordinates into our slope formula:

$$slope = \frac{y_2 - y_1}{x_2 - x_1}$$

$$slope = \frac{5-2}{3-1}$$

$$slope = \frac{3}{2}$$

6

Example #2

Point 1 = (1,8)
Point 2 = (6,2)

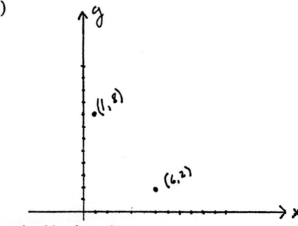

Drawing the line determined by the points:

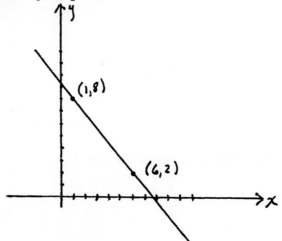

Calculating the slope:

$$slope = \frac{y_2 - y_1}{x_2 - x_1}$$

$$slope = \frac{2-8}{6-1}$$

$$slope = -\frac{6}{5}$$

There are several very important points about our two examples that should be mentioned here.

First

Notice that in the first example the slope of the line was a positive number and in the second example the slope was a negative number.

A line that slopes upward as you move to the right has a positive slope

A line that slopes downward as you move to the right has a negative slope

Second

In both examples, it does not matter which one we call point 1 or point 2. If we reverse them and again insert the coordinates into the slope equation, we will still get a slope of 3/2 for Example #1 and a slope of – 6/5 for Example #2. The slope of the line is an intrinsic characteristic of the line itself.

There is one more important example before we move on to how to interpret the slope.

Example #3

Point 1 = (2,3)
Point 2 = (5,3)

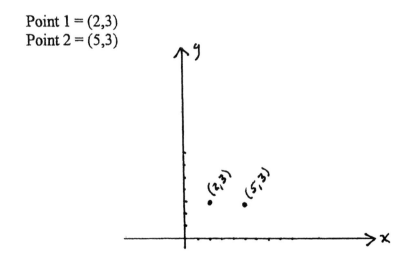

Again, drawing the line through the two points:

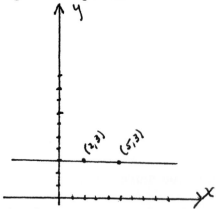

Notice that because both points have the same y-coordinate the line drawn is horizontal. Calculating the slope:

$$slope = \frac{y_2 - y_1}{x_2 - x_1}$$

$$slope = \frac{3-3}{5-2}$$

$$slope = \frac{0}{3} = 0$$

A horizontal line has zero slope

Interpretation of the Slope

The first interpretation of the slope of a line is as a measurement of the steepness of the line. In the following diagram, line #1 is much steeper than line #2:

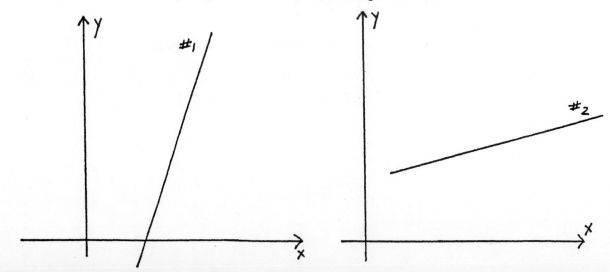

If we calculated the slope of both lines, we would find that line #1 does indeed have a larger slope than line #2.

The second interpretation of the slope is at the heart of differential calculus and at the heart of the concept of a functional derivative. Because of its fundamental importance to a true understanding of differential calculus, an entire section has been devoted to it.

Slope as a Rate of Change

Let's consider two lines given by two different sets of points:

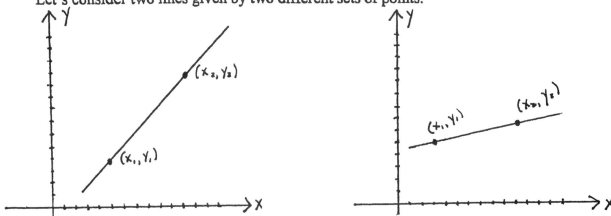

Remember that x_1 and x_2 are the distances, respectively, of each of our points along the x-axis.

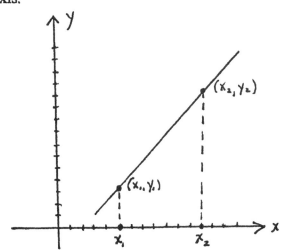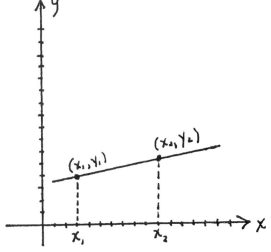

Notice that, in each case, as we move from x_1 to x_2, our y-coordinate changes from y_1 to y_2:

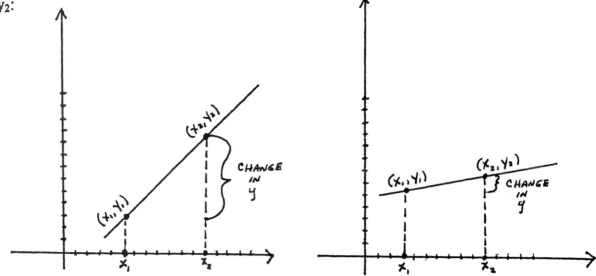

For line #1, whose slope is larger than line #2, we get a much larger change in the y-coordinate as we move from x_1 to x_2, than for line #2.

The larger the slope of the line, the larger the change in y as we change x

In other words,

> The slope of a line is a measurement of how the y-coordinate changes with respect to the x-coordinate. A line with a large slope has a large change in y if you change x (as in line #1); a line with a small slope has a small change in y if you change x (as in line #2).

If we again write our slope expression:

$$slope = \frac{y_2 - y_1}{x_2 - x_1}$$

we can also see the interpretation of the slope as the change in the y-coordinate as we change the x-coordinate. The numerator is the change in the y-coordinate and the denominator is the change in the x-coordinate. In mathematics, it is common to use the capital Greek letter delta, Δ, as a shorthand way of writing "change". Using this shorthand, we can write our slope expression as:

$$slope = \frac{\Delta y}{\Delta x}$$

Now that we understand a little bit about how to calculate the slopes of lines and how to interpret the slopes that we calculate, let's generalize it a little bit.

Dependent and Independent Variables

Suppose that we have an equation such as y = 2x +3. The two variables, x and y, in the equation are given names. Since we have complete freedom to choose any number to insert for the variable x, we say that x is the **independent variable**. Although we had the freedom to choose any number that we wished for x, once this number is chosen, y is **fixed**. The variable y is completely dependent on the number inserted for x. Because of this, y is said to be the **dependent variable**.

For example, if x is chosen to be 1 and inserted into our equation:

$$y = 2(1) + 3$$
$$y = 5$$

or, if x is chosen to be 2 and inserted:

$$y = 2(2) + 3$$
$$y = 7$$

y is completely determined once we have chosen our x

This new way of looking at the relationship between x and y is **extremely** useful and extends to other variables as well. In the equation

$$s = 3t^2 + 4t$$

t is the independent variable and s is the dependent variable. The variable s is completely determined once a value of t has been chosen.

All of the graphs thus far have been in terms of x and y. Since our long-term goal is to be able to apply the concepts of differential calculus to real-life situations, it is beneficial to us to rethink the way in which we set up our coordinate axes.

> In graphing an equation it is useful to place the independent variable on the horizontal axis and the dependent variable on the vertical axis

For example, suppose we know that in a certain section of an electric circuit the current i that flows through it changes with time according to

$$i = 3t + 2$$

Notice that the current that is flowing through that section of the circuit depends on the time at which we look at the section. In other words, t is our independent variable and i is our dependent variable. Graphing our equation:

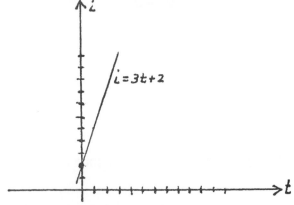

If we choose two times to look at the circuit, $t = 1$ and $t = 2$, we can find the current flowing at those two times:

$$t = 1 \rightarrow i = 3(1) + 2 = 5$$
$$t = 2 \rightarrow i = 3(2) + 2 = 8$$

We moved one unit on our horizontal axis (we went from $t = 1$ sec to $t = 2$ sec). As a result of this, we went from 5 amps of current to 8 amps of current (our vertical axis). In other words, we get a change of 3 amps for every 1 sec of time.

> The current is changing at the rate of 3 amps/1 sec

If we instead take the two coordinates of the two points with which we have been dealing:

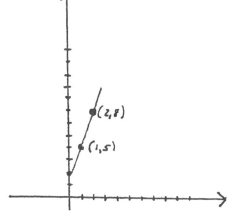

and calculate the slope of the line using them:

$$slope = \frac{i_2 - i_1}{t_2 - t_1}$$

$$slope = \frac{8amps - 5amps}{2\sec - 1\sec}$$

$$slope = \frac{3amps}{1\sec}$$

The slope calculation verifies our intuition that the current is changing at the rate of 3amps/sec. It may seem as if we are belaboring the point, but a true understanding that the slope of the line is the rate of change of the dependent variable with respect to the independent variable is **necessary** for a complete understanding of the concept of the derivative.

Our next section involves a slight change in notation. **We are not changing our concept of slope!** We are only changing our notation slightly to help facilitate our motivation of the ideas behind a functional derivative.

Functional Notation

There are times when it is more convenient **not** to actually give the vertical axis (our dependent variable) a variable such as y. There are many instances where it is advantageous to note, instead, that it is a function of a certain independent variable. For example, in a previous section, we dealt with the equation:

$$y = 3x + 2$$

Where y was the dependent variable, and x was the independent variable. There is an alternate way of writing down the same function:

$$f(x) = 3x + 2$$

The left-hand side of the above expression **does not** mean f multiplied by x. It is the notation that we use to express the fact that the expression is a function of the independent variable x.

We pronounce the left-hand side as "f of x"

We graph the function just as we did before, this time labeling the vertical axis as $f(x)$ instead of y:

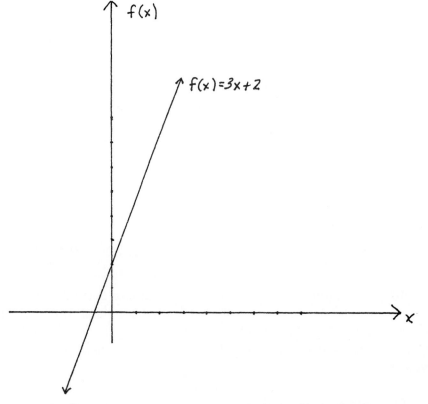

One of the advantageous of this notation is the evaluation of our vertical coordinates using our horizontal coordinates. Suppose that we have the following function:

$$f(x) = 2x + 1$$

and we want to know the value of the function at x = 1. We simply insert the value of 1 everywhere in our function that we see an x:

$$f(1) = 2(1) + 1$$
$$f(1) = 3$$

We read this as "f of one is equal to three" or "the function evaluated at the point one is equal to three".

Although we could just as easily inserted the value of 1 into our equation when it was in the form:

$$y = 2x + 1$$

our new notation, on its left-hand side, points out for us the value of the independent variable that we inserted, in this case a 1. Because this new notation is going to simplify our derivation of the functional derivative, we are going to spend a little more time understanding it.

We can evaluate our function at any point that we wish. To express the fact that we are evaluating our function at a particular value, we place it inside the parentheses beside the *f* on the left-hand side of the equation. For example, if we have the function:

$$f(x) = 5x - 7$$

and we would like to evaluate it at a value of 4. We insert the 4 into the parentheses to tell us the value that we are inserting, and then insert a 4 everywhere that we see an *x* in our expression:

$$f(4) = 5(4) - 7$$
$$f(4) = 20 - 7$$
$$f(4) = 13$$

We can insert almost anything we wish into our function, including other letters! All we do is put it between the parentheses to inform us what we are inserting, and then substitute it everywhere we see an x in the function

Suppose that, this time, instead of inserting a number such as 4, we insert the letter p:

$$f(p) = 5(p) - 7$$
$$f(p) = 5p - 7$$

We'll do one more example and then continue on toward our definition of a functional derivative. Suppose that, in our same function, we decide to insert $(x + 2)$:

$$f(x+2) = 5(x+2) - 7$$
$$f(x+2) = 5x + 5(2) - 7$$
$$f(x+2) = 5x + 10 - 7$$
$$f(x+2) = 5x + 3$$

This new way of writing our functions can now be coupled with the previously discussed topic of slope. Let's return to our graph with the two generic points (x_1, y_1) and (x_2, y_2):

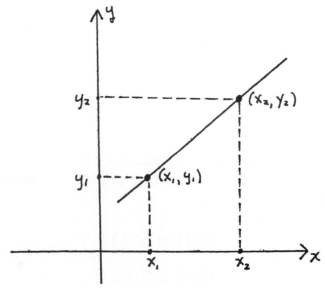

Since we now know that we can generate the vertical coordinate given the horizontal coordinate using our new notation, we do not have to be given y_1 and y_2. If we know x_1 we can generate the vertical coordinate that is associated with it by inserting x_1 into our function, in other words, by finding $f(x_1)$. We can likewise find the vertical coordinate associated with x_2 by finding $f(x_2)$. Let's again plot our two generic points and the line that can be drawn through them, this time labeling the vertical coordinates with our new notation:

We can still find the slope of our line, remembering that the slope is the difference in the vertical coordinates divided by the difference in the horizontal coordinates. This time, however, we have to be careful to use our new way of writing down our vertical coordinates:

$$slope = \frac{f(x_2) - f(x_1)}{x_2 - x_1}$$

The interpretation of the slope remains the same. In this case, since it is the value of the function $f(x)$ that is on the vertical axis:

> The slope is the rate at which the value of the function is changing as we move from x_1 to x_2

After all of these pages of background,

WE ARE FINALLY AT THE STAGE TO BEGIN DISCUSSING DERIVATIVES!

Exercises

In the following equations, identify the dependent and independent variable:

1. $y = 5x^2 - 7x$

2. $B = 7t^3$

3. $R = 3w + 8$

4. $E = 9s - 11$

Given the following sets of points, calculate the slope of the line that would pass through the points:

5. $(4,2), (3,1)$

6. $(2,5), (8,1)$

7. $(3,5), (9,5)$

8. $(0,0), (2,6)$

For each of the following functions, find $f(0)$ and $f(1)$:

9. $f(x) = 2x$

10. $f(x) = 3x^2$

11. $f(x) = 9 - 4x$

12. $f(x) = 4x^2 + 5x$

Answers

	Independent	**Dependent**
1.	x	y
2.	t	B
3.	w	R
4.	s	E

5. Slope = 1

6. Slope = -2/3

7. Slope = 0

8. Slope = 3

	f(0)	**f(1)**
9.	0	2
10.	0	3
11.	0	5
12.	0	9

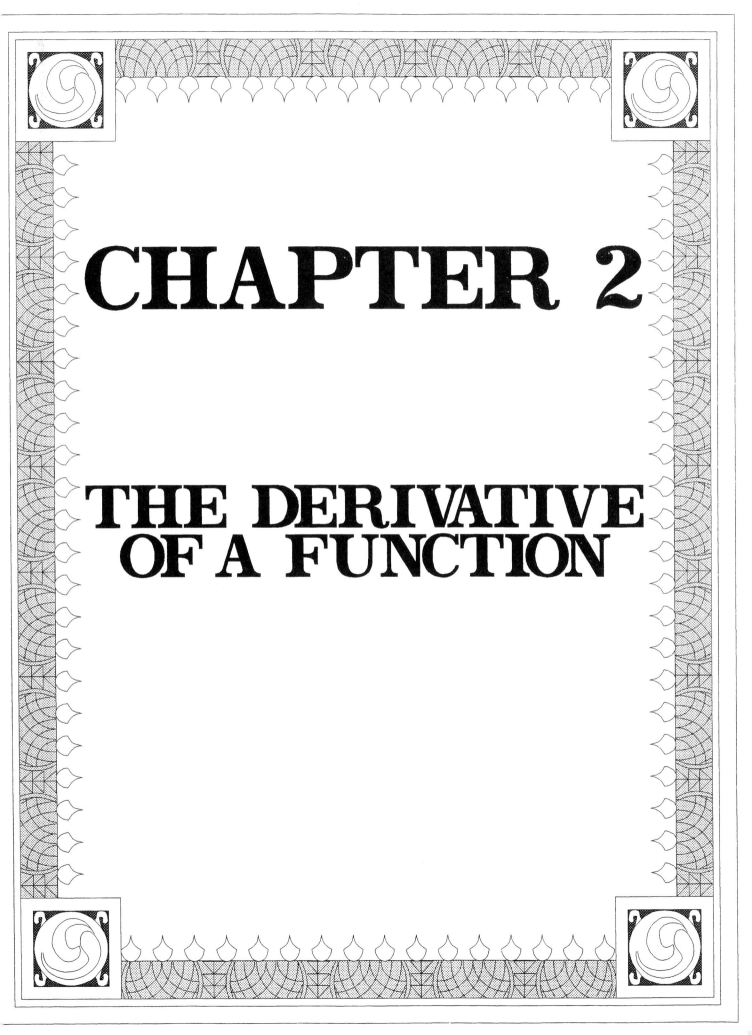

CHAPTER 2

THE DERIVATIVE OF A FUNCTION

The Derivative of a Function

Even thought almost all of the graphs that we have been dealing with have been straight lines, in real world situations it is rare to find two quantities that are related in a linear fashion (in other words their graph is a straight line). We want to be able to discuss quantities that are related to one another in non-linear ways **and to be able to discuss the rate at which the dependent quantity is changing with respect to the independent quantity**.

Suppose that we have a sample function such as the following:

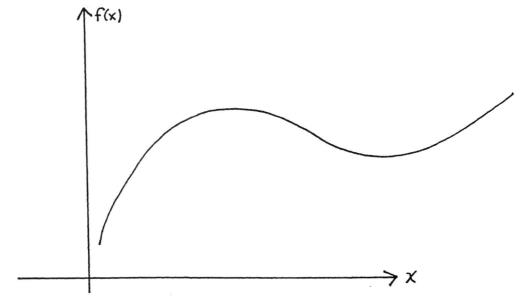

Let's choose two points and label them using coordinates:

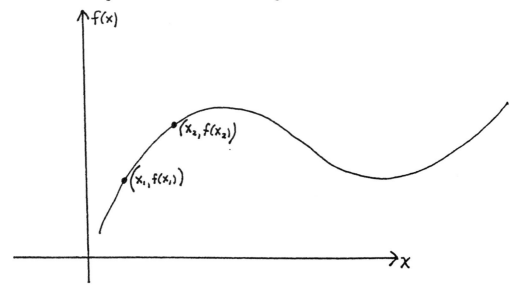

24

Now let's draw the tangent lines through our two generic points:

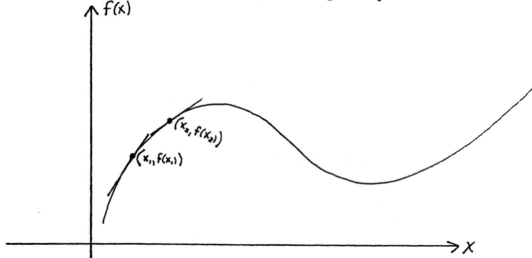

Remember that a tangent line is a line drawn that intersects a curve in one and only one point as in the following diagram:

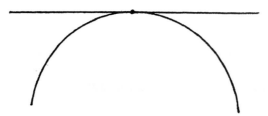

Looking again at our function with the two generic points and their respective tangent lines, we note that the slope of the tangent line at point #1 is much larger than the slope of the tangent line at point #2. What this means is that our dependent variable is changing at a much larger rate at point #1 than at point #2.

We now, finally, are at the stage where we can introduce the concept of a derivative.

The following two statements are the two most important ways to think about and interpret the derivative of a function. You will have a much clearer understanding of the derivative if you keep these two statements in the back of your mind:

1.	The derivative of a function, at a particular point on the function, is the rate at which the dependent variable is changing with respect to the independent variable, at that same point.
2.	The derivative of a function, at a particular point, is the slope of the tangent line to the function, drawn at that same point.

Just as in dealing with the slope, there is a difference between being able to interpret the derivative of a function, and being able to actually calculate the derivative. In addition to the work that we have done acquiring a complete understanding of slope, we need to understand the idea of the **limit** of a function before we can actually **calculate** the derivative of a function.

The Limit of a Function

The limit of a function is the value that the function takes on as you let the independent variable get closer and closer to a particular value.

Suppose that we have the function f(x) = 3x + 2. What value wold this function take on if we let the variable x get closer and closer to 1? Let's chart out the response of the function f(x) as we let x get closer to 1 starting from **5**:

$$x = 5 : f(5) = 3(5) + 2 = 17$$
$$x = 4 : f(4) = 3(4) + 2 = 14$$
$$x = 3 : f(3) = 3(3) + 2 = 11$$
$$x = 2 : f(2) = 3(2) + 2 = 8$$
$$x = 1 : f(1) = 3(1) + 2 = 5$$

The limit of the function f(x) as x approaches 1 is 5

Ok, we approached x = 1 from values to the right of it and we arrived at a value for the function of **5**. Suppose that we start with values to the left of x = 1:

$$x = -2 : f(-2) = 3(-2) + 2 = -4$$
$$x = -1 : f(-1) : 3(-1) + 2 = -1$$
$$x = 0 : f(0) = 3(0) + 2 = 2$$
$$x = 1 : f(1) = 3(1) + 2 = 5$$

In other words, provided that our function changes smoothly, the direction in which we approach our value for the independent variable does not affect the final value of the function. If we approached x = 1 from the right, the function had a value of 5, and if we approached x = 1 from the left, the function again had a value of 5. Here is how, in mathematical language, we write the fact that the limit as x approached 1 was 5:

$$\lim_{x \to 1} 3x + 2 = 5$$

You may be asking yourself why we go through the bother to chart out the approach toward the value for the independent variable. Wouldn't it be easier to just insert the value of the independent variable in which we are interested into the function? It would appear that all we really had to do in the last example was to insert 1 into our function and 5 is the answer. **The next example will show how the limit of a function differs from simple insertion of a value of the independent variable.**

Example #1

Suppose, now, that our function is f(x) = 1/x and we are interested in the limit of this function as x gets closer and closer to x = 0. If we wanted to write this out using our symbols:

$$\lim_{x \to 0} \frac{1}{x} = ?$$

This example illustrates how the concept of a limit differs from simple numerical insertion. We are not allowed to simply insert the value of x = 0 into our function since this would mean that we would be dividing by zero.

However, even though we cannot directly insert zero, we can get as close to it as we wish. **This is the idea of a limit.**

What value does the function take on as our independent variable comes very close to a certain value?

Although we cannot directly insert the value of zero for x in our function, we can let x get smaller and smaller. Remember that if the denominator of a fraction gets smaller the fraction itself gets larger. As we let x get very close to zero (extremely small) our fraction $1/x$ becomes extremely large. If we let x get infinitely close to zero, our function becomes infinitely large. Writing this as an equation:

$$\lim_{x \to 0} \frac{1}{x} = \infty$$

The theory behind the limits of functions is a very large area in and of itself. Our purpose, however, is to learn enough about limits in order to learn how to calculate the derivative of a function. The idea that the limit of a function is the value of the function as our independent variable approaches a certain value is sufficient for our purposes. Let's use what we have learned about limits and move into how to actually calculate the derivative of a function.

Calculating the Derivative of a Function

As we begin this section, do not lose sight of our two ways of thinking about the derivative, first as the slope of the tangent line drawn at a certain point on our function, and second as the rate of change of the dependent variable with respect to the independent variable.

Suppose that we have a function such as the following:

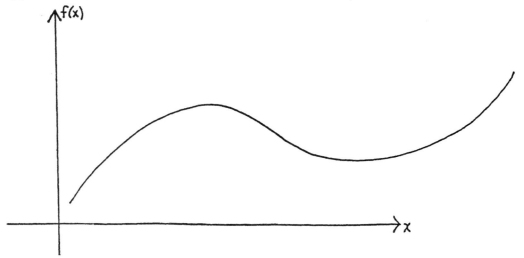

Let's choose a point x on our function to analyze and label it with its coordinates, remembering to use f(x) as our vertical coordinate:

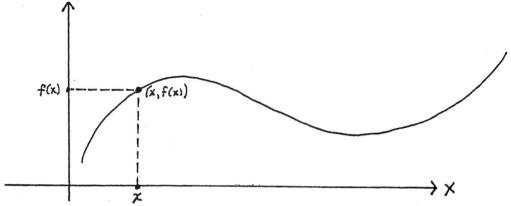

Then draw the tangent line to the function at our point:

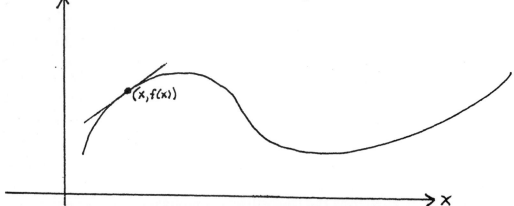

Since the slope of the tangent line at this point <u>is</u> the derivative of the function at this point, to calculate the derivative we must find the slope of our tangent line.

Let's start by taking two points, one to the left of the point in which we are interested, and one to the right:

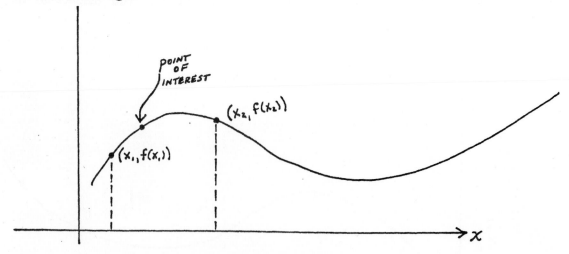

If we draw the line defined by our two points:

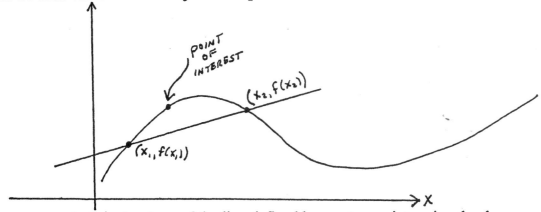

We can calculate the slope of the line defined by our two points using the slope equation that we have used many times before:

$$slope = \frac{f(x_2) - f(x_1)}{x_2 - x_1}$$

Our next step is to rewrite slightly our horizontal coordinate. Instead of calling the first horizontal coordinate x_1, let's simply call it x. Since x_2 is a certain distance farther down the x-axis, let's call that distance Δx, we can express the second horizontal coordinate as $x + \Delta x$:

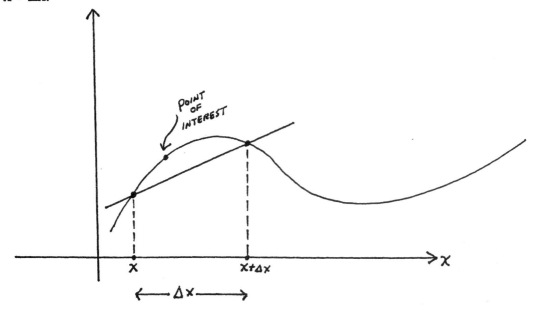

Since the vertical coordinates can be generated by inserting the horizontal values into our function, we can express the coordinates of our two points after our rewrite as:

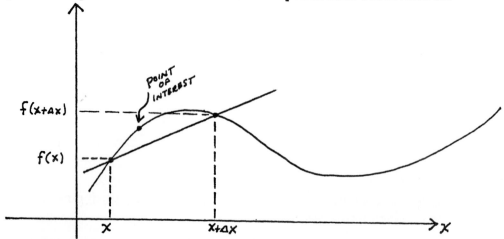

If we again calculate the slope of the line determined by the two points:

$$slope = \frac{f(x+\Delta x) - f(x)}{(x+\Delta x) - x} = \frac{f(x+\Delta x) - f(x)}{\Delta x}$$

The slope of the line determined by our two points gives us an approximation to the slope of the line in which we are actually interested, namely the slope of the tangent line to the curve. It is obvious that this is not a very good approximation. We can make the approximation better, however, by choosing our two points closer to our point of interest:

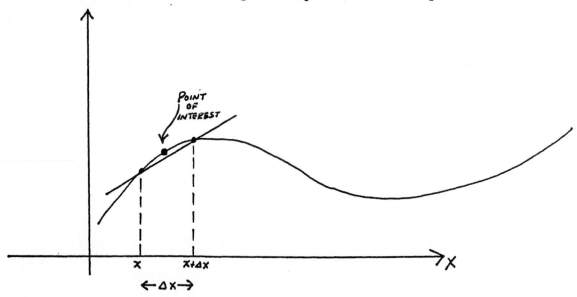

If we again calculate the slope of the line determined by the two points, this slope is nearer to the slope of the tangent line. We can, again, improve the approximation by choosing two points still closer to our point of interest and calculating the slope of the line determined by them:

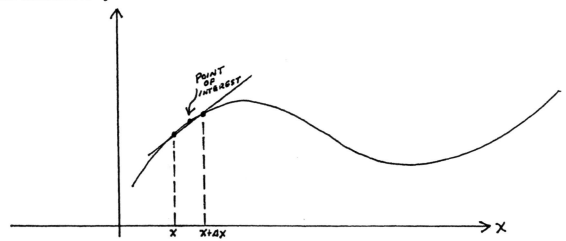

As you can see, the closer that we choose our two points to our point of interest, the better the approximation to the slope of the tangent line to our function. This is where we use the concept of the limit. Suppose we allow our two points to get closer and closer together. Let's choose our two points so close together that they are infinitely close to our point of interest. Since Δx represents the distance between our two points, requiring that the two points be infinitely close together is the same as having Δx approach zero. In other words,

> If we take the limit of our slope equation as Δx approaches zero, we will have a way to calculate the slope of the tangent line to the function at our point. Since finding the slope of the tangent line is the same thing as finding the derivative of the function, we will have a means of calculating the derivative of the function.

If we write out the above in the language of mathematics:

The derivative of the function f(x) is

$$\lim_{\Delta x \to 0} \frac{f(x + \Delta x) - f(x)}{\Delta x}$$

We use f '(x) as a short-hand way of writing the derivative of a function:

$$f'(x) = \lim_{\Delta x \to 0} \frac{f(x + \Delta x) - f(x)}{\Delta x}$$

Ok, we have an equation that supposedly will allow us to calculate the derivative of a function. The questions now are:

1) **For a specific function, how do we use our equation to calculate the derivative?**
2) **Once we calculate this derivative, what have we actually found?**

We will deal with these questions in order. Let's take a specific function and use our equation to calculate its derivative.

Example #2

Suppose that we have the function $f(x) = x^2$:

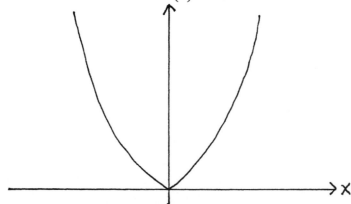

Let's use our definition of the derivative to calculate the derivative of this function. The definition of the derivative is a recipe for finding the derivative. We have to insert into our definition $f(x + \Delta x)$ and $f(x)$ for our particular function.

Remember from our section on functional notation, $f(x + \Delta x)$ means that we are going to take our function, $f(x) = x^2$, and insert $(x + \Delta x)$ everywhere that we see an x. For our function,

$$f(x + \Delta x) = (x + \Delta x)^2$$

In the definition, we must insert the above expression in for $f(x + \Delta x)$. We also have to replace $f(x)$ in the definition with the expression for our original function $f(x) = x^2$.

Starting from the definition and inserting the values of $f(x)$ and $f(x + \Delta x)$ into to:

$$f'(x) = \lim_{\Delta x \to 0} \frac{(x + \Delta x)^2 - x^2}{\Delta x}$$

$$\Rightarrow f'(x) = \lim_{\Delta x \to 0} \frac{f(x + \Delta x) - f(x)}{\Delta x}$$

Our task now is to simplify the right-hand side of the definition. Unfortunately, we cannot yet take the limit as Δx approached zero merely by inserting zero. We are confronted with the same situation as the function that we analyzed in our section on limits. If we simply inserted zero into the definition where we see Δx, we would be dividing by zero. We must use a little algebra to simplify the right-hand side before we can take the limit. First, let's expand the squared term:

$$f'(x) = \lim_{\Delta x \to 0} \frac{(x^2 + 2x\Delta x + \Delta x^2) - x^2}{\Delta x} = \lim_{\Delta x \to 0} \frac{2x\Delta x + \Delta x^2}{\Delta x}$$

Now factor Δx off of each of the terms in the numerator:

$$f'(x) = \lim_{\Delta x \to 0} \frac{\Delta x(2x + \Delta x)}{\Delta x}$$

We can now cancel the Δx between the numerator and the denominator:

$$f'(x) = \lim_{\Delta x \to 0} 2x + \Delta x$$

With this cancellation, we are now in the position where taking the limit will not involve us dividing by zero. We can now take the limit by simply inserting zero everywhere that we see Δx:

$$f'(x) = \lim_{\Delta x \to 0} 2x + \Delta x$$

$$f'(x) = 2x + 0$$

$$f'(x) = 2x$$

The derivative of the function f(x) = x² is 2x. We just calculated our first derivative!!

Now that we have calculated the derivative, we must answer the second question:

What have we actually found?

The derivative of the function is supposed to be the slope of the tangent line drawn at a particular point on the function. When we find the derivative of the function, for example in our case,

$$f'(x) = 2x$$

we have found an expression that will give us the slope of the tangent line at any point along our function in which we are interested. For example, suppose that for our function, $f(x) = x^2$, we are interested in the slope of the tangent line that can be drawn at $x = 2$:

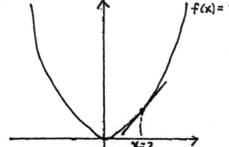

To find the slope of the tangent line at $x = 2$ we insert the point 2 into our derivative:

$$f'(x) = 2x$$

$$f'(2) = 2(2)$$

$$f'(2) = 4$$

The slope of the tangent line at x = 2 is 4.

Suppose now that we are interested in the slope of the tangent line to the function that can be drawn at $x = 3$:

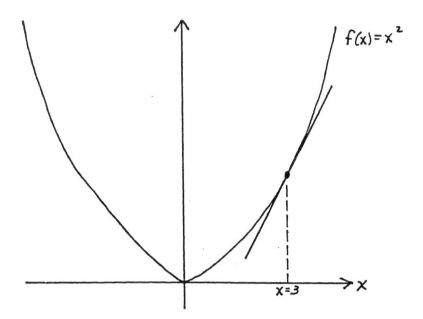

To find the slope of this tangent line, we insert the point 3 into our derivative:

$$f'(x) = 2x$$

$$f'(3) = 2(3)$$

$$f'(3) = 6$$

The slope of the tangent line to the function drawn at x = 3 is 6.

To summarize what we have done thus far:

1) We use our definition of the derivative of a function:

$$f'(x) = \lim_{\Delta x \to 0} \frac{f(x + \Delta x) - f(x)}{\Delta x}$$

as a step-by-step recipe for calculating the derivative of the function. Because of the Δx that is in the denominator of the definition, we will normally have to do some algebra before we can actually take the limit as Δx approaches zero.

2) Once we have an expression for the derivative of a function, we can find the slope of the tangent line at any point along the function by inserting that value of x into our derivative.

Let's do another example.

Example #3

$f(x) = x^3$

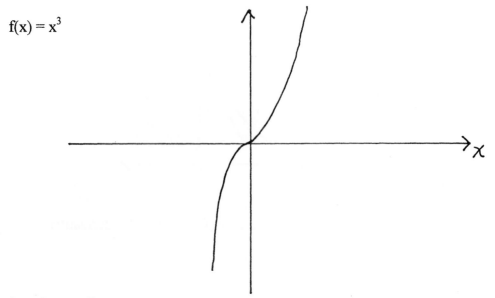

Remember that to find the derivative, we always have to substitute into our definition what f(x + Δx) is for our particular function. In this case,

$$f(x + \Delta x) = (x + \Delta x)^3$$

Starting from our definition and inserting f(x + Δx) and f(x) for this example:

$$f'(x) = \lim_{\Delta x \to 0} \frac{f(x + \Delta x) - f(x)}{\Delta x}$$

$$f'(x) = \lim_{\Delta x \to 0} \frac{(x + \Delta x)^3 - x^3}{\Delta x}$$

We are once again in the position where we cannot directly substitute zero in for Δx because this would involve us dividing by zero. Algebra is required to simplify the equation. If we expand the cubed term:

$$f'(x) = \lim_{\Delta x \to 0} \frac{(x^3 + 3x^2 \Delta x + 3x \Delta x^2 + \Delta x^3) - x^3}{\Delta x}$$

$$f'(x) = \lim_{\Delta x \to 0} \frac{3x^2 \Delta x + 3x \Delta x^2 + \Delta x^3}{\Delta x}$$

Factoring off Δx from each of the terms in the numerator:

$$f'(x) = \lim_{\Delta x \to 0} \frac{\Delta x(3x^2 + 3x\Delta x + \Delta x^2)}{\Delta x}$$

Canceling Δx between numerator and denominator:

$$f'(x) = \lim_{\Delta x \to 0} 3x^2 + 3x\Delta x + \Delta x^2$$

Now that Δx is no longer in the denominator we can take the limit by inserting zero for Δx:

$$f'(x) = 3x^2 + 3x(0) + (0)^2$$
$$f'(x) = 3x^2$$

The derivative of the function f(x) = x³ is 3x².

If we now would like to know the slope of the tangent line that can be drawn at, for example, x = 1, we substitute 1 into our derivative everywhere that we see an *x*:

$$f'(x) = 3x^2$$
$$f'(1) = 3(1)^2$$
$$f'(1) = 3$$

The slope of the tangent line to the function drawn at x = 1 is equal to three.

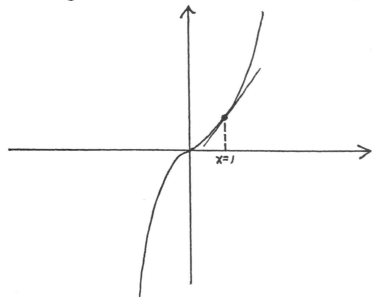

Exercises

Use the definition of the derivative:

$$f'(x) = \lim_{\Delta x \to 0} \frac{f(x + \Delta x) - f(x)}{\Delta x}$$

to find the derivative of the following functions:

1.

$$f(x) = 2x$$

2.

$$f(x) = x^2$$

3.

$$f(x) = 5x - 3$$

4.

$$f(x) = x^3$$

5.

$$f(x) = 6x^2 + 7x$$

SOLUTIONS

1.   First we find f (x + Δx) for our function so that it can be inserted into our definition:

$$f(x + \Delta x) = 2(x + \Delta x)$$

Next, we insert our terms into our definition:

$$f'(x) = \lim_{\Delta x \to 0} \frac{f(x + \Delta x) - f(x)}{\Delta x}$$

$$f'(x) = \lim_{\Delta x \to 0} \frac{2(x + \Delta x) - 2x}{\Delta x}$$

$$f'(x) = \lim_{\Delta x \to 0} \frac{2x + 2\Delta x - 2x}{\Delta x}$$

$$f'(x) = \lim_{\Delta x \to 0} \frac{2\Delta x}{\Delta x}$$

$$f'(x) = \lim_{\Delta x \to 0} 2$$

Since there is no Δx in our expression, the limit does not affect our answer:

$$f'(x) = 2$$

2.   For this function:

$$f(x + \Delta x) = (x + \Delta x)^2$$

Inserting the terms into our definition:

$$f'(x) = \lim_{\Delta x \to 0} \frac{f(x + \Delta x) - f(x)}{\Delta x}$$

$$f'(x) = \lim_{\Delta x \to 0} \frac{(x + \Delta x)^2 - x^2}{\Delta x}$$

$$f'(x) = \lim_{\Delta x \to 0} \frac{x^2 + 2x\Delta x + \Delta x^2 - x^2}{\Delta x}$$

$$f'(x) = \lim_{\Delta x \to 0} \frac{2x\Delta x + \Delta x^2}{\Delta x}$$

$$f'(x) = \lim_{\Delta x \to 0} \frac{\Delta x(2x + \Delta x)}{\Delta x}$$

$$f'(x) = \lim_{\Delta x \to 0} (2x + \Delta x)$$

$$f'(x) = 2x$$

3. For this function:

$$f(x + \Delta x) = 5(x + \Delta x) - 3$$

Inserting our terms into the definition:

$$f'(x) = \lim_{\Delta x \to 0} \frac{f(x + \Delta x) - f(x)}{\Delta x}$$

$$f'(x) = \lim_{\Delta x \to 0} \frac{5(x + \Delta x) - 3 - (5x - 3)}{\Delta x}$$

$$f'(x) = \lim_{\Delta x \to 0} \frac{5x + 5\Delta x - 3 - 5x + 3}{\Delta x}$$

$$f'(x) = \lim_{\Delta x \to 0} \frac{5\Delta x}{\Delta x}$$

$$f'(x) = \lim_{\Delta x \to 0} 5$$

$$f'(x) = 5$$

4. In this case:

$$f(x + \Delta x) = (x + \Delta x)^3$$

Inserting the terms into our definition:

$$f'(x) = \lim_{\Delta x \to 0} \frac{(x + \Delta x)^3 - x^3}{\Delta x}$$

Expanding the cubed term:

$$f'(x) = \lim_{\Delta x \to 0} \frac{(x^3 + 3x^2\Delta x + 3x\Delta x^2 + \Delta x^3) - x^3}{\Delta x}$$

$$f'(x) = \lim_{\Delta x \to 0} \frac{x^3 + 3x^2\Delta x + 3x\Delta x^2 + \Delta x^3 - x^3}{\Delta x}$$

$$f'(x) = \lim_{\Delta x \to 0} \frac{3x^2\Delta x + 3x\Delta x^2 + \Delta x^3}{\Delta x}$$

$$f'(x) = \lim_{\Delta x \to 0} \frac{\Delta x(3x^2 + 3x\Delta x + \Delta x^2)}{\Delta x}$$

$$f'(x) = \lim_{\Delta x \to 0} 3x^2 + 3x\Delta x + \Delta x^2$$

$$f'(x) = 3x^2$$

5.   For this last function:

$$f(x + \Delta x) = 6(x + \Delta x)^2 + 7(x + \Delta x)$$

Setting up our definition:

$$f'(x) = \lim_{\Delta x \to 0} \frac{f(x + \Delta x) - f(x)}{\Delta x}$$

$$f'(x) = \lim_{\Delta x \to 0} \frac{6(x + \Delta x)^2 + 7(x + \Delta x) - (6x^2 + 7x)}{\Delta x}$$

Executing the appropriate algebra:

$$f'(x) = \lim_{\Delta x \to 0} \frac{6(x^2 + 2x\Delta x + \Delta x^2) + 7(x + \Delta x) - 6x^2 - 7x}{\Delta x}$$

$$f'(x) = \lim_{\Delta x \to 0} \frac{6x^2 + 12x\Delta x + 6\Delta x^2 + 7x + 7\Delta x - 6x^2 - 7x}{\Delta x}$$

$$f'(x) = \lim_{\Delta x \to 0} \frac{12x\Delta x + 6\Delta x^2 + 7\Delta x}{\Delta x}$$

$$f'(x) = \lim_{\Delta x \to 0} \frac{\Delta x(12x + 6\Delta x + 7)}{\Delta x}$$

$$f'(x) = \lim_{\Delta x \to 0} 12x + 6\Delta x + 7$$

$$f'(x) = 12x + 7$$

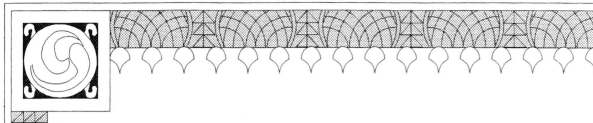

CHAPTER 3

SHORTCUTS FOR FINDING THE DERIVATIVES OF SOME BASIC FUNCTIONS

From the two examples in the previous section, we see that calculating derivatives starting from our definition is a rather difficult and time-consuming thing. We were forced into several steps of simplification and algebra in order to get to our goal. If we had to go through that many steps in order to calculate the derivatives of functions as simple as $f(x) = x^2$ and $f(x) = x^3$, you can imagine how difficult the algebra becomes if we deal with functions such as $f(x) = (x^3 + 5x^2 + 3)(4x^2 - 7x + 11)$!!

Because our eventual goal is to be able to apply the concept of a derivative to real world situations, such as projectile motion and circuit analysis, we need to find a much quicker and simpler way of calculating derivatives than starting from the definition

This section is devoted to showing much easier and faster ways of calculating functional derivatives, rather than starting from our formal definition. Different types of functions, for example simple polynomials and trigonometric functions, have different shortcuts for finding the derivative. Because we do not know what sorts of functions may arise in the physical problems that we will be trying to solve, we need to be able to handle whatever functions we might meet.

The shortcuts that we will now be covering are tricks! We could still use the formal definition of the derivative on these functions to find the derivative.

If we find the derivative of a function using our shortcuts instead of the formal definition, we still have found an expression that will give us the slope of the tangent line to the function drawn at a point. The way that we think about derivatives has not changed, only the method that we are using to calculate them.

Trick #1 – Simple Polynomials

Let's start with the function $f(x) = 3x^2 + 4$ and find the derivative using our definition. Once we have found the derivative, we will use our shortcut and verify that the answers are the same.

Starting from our definition:

$$f'(x) = \lim_{\Delta x \to 0} \frac{f(x + \Delta x) - f(x)}{\Delta x}$$

Inserting $f(x + \Delta x)$ and $f(x)$:

$$f'(x) = \lim_{\Delta x \to 0} \frac{3(x + \Delta x)^2 + 4 - (3x^2 + 4)}{\Delta x}$$

Expanding the squared term:

$$f'(x) = \lim_{\Delta x \to 0} \frac{3(x^2 + 2x\Delta x + \Delta x^2) + 4 - 3x^2 - 4}{\Delta x}$$

Distributing through the 3 that is multiplying the parentheses:

$$f'(x) = \lim_{\Delta x \to 0} \frac{3x^2 + 6x\Delta x + 3\Delta x^2 + 4 - 3x^2 - 4}{\Delta x}$$

We are now in the position that some of the terms in the numerator cancel. **Notice that the constant term of 4 cancels at this stage. This will be very important to us when we learn the shortcut for polynomials.** After canceling terms:

$$f'(x) = \lim_{\Delta x \to 0} \frac{6x\Delta x + 3\Delta x^2}{\Delta x}$$

Factoring Δx off of each of the terms in the numerator:

$$f'(x) = \lim_{\Delta x \to 0} \frac{\Delta x(6x + 3x\Delta x)}{\Delta x}$$

Canceling the Δx between numerator and denominator:

$$f'(x) = \lim_{\Delta x \to 0} 6x + 3\Delta x$$

Taking the limit as Δx approaches zero:

$$f'(x) = 6x + 3(0)$$
$$f'(x) = 6x$$

The derivative of $f(x) = 3x^2 + 4$ is $6x$

Now that we know what the correct derivative is supposed to be, let's learn our first shortcut. This shortcut is only for simple polynomials. Different types of functions require different shortcuts.

The shortcut for simple polynomials:

1)	Term-by-term, take the exponent on the term, bring it down and make it a coefficient in front of the term, and lower the exponent by one power.
2)	Remember that when we used the definition the 4 cancelled. The derivative of any constant is zero.

Let's use our shortcut and see if it reproduces the same derivative as the formal definition. Starting with our function:

$$f(x) = 3x^2 + 4$$

we will deal with the $3x^2$ term first. Our shortcut says that we are supposed to take the exponent, in this case a 2, and bring it down in front of the term. Since there is already a 3 sitting in front of the term, we will be multiplying the 2 and 3 together. We are also supposed to take the exponent, in this case a 2, and lower it by one power. Writing all of this out, the derivative of the $3x^2$ portion of our function becomes:

$$2(3)x^{2-1}$$

Simplifying our expression:

$$6x$$

The derivative of the $3x^2$ portion of our function is 6x

Now we must deal with the constant term of 4 in our function. There are two ways for us to think about this term. Both ways yield the same result, although the first way is a little bit more difficult.

The First Way

Remember that we can write the number 4 as:

$$4 = 4x^0$$

since anything raised to the zero power is equal to one. Using our shortcuts, this would mean that we would be bringing down a zero to multiply our term if we took the derivative. Since we would be multiplying by zero, this would mean that the derivative of 4 would vanish.

<u>The Second Way</u>

It is a little simpler to remember that the derivative of any constant term (any term without a variable beside it) is **zero**.

Putting both of our pieces together:

$$f(x) = 3x^2 + 4$$
$$f'(x) = 6x + 0$$
$$f'(x) = 6x$$

It works! The shortcut reproduced the same derivative as the formal definition.

Let's use our shortcut and do a few examples.

Example #1

Find the derivative of the function $f(x) = 5x^3 + 4x^2 + 7x + 3$

We will use our shortcut, term-by-term, on our function. For each of the terms, we will take its exponent and bring it down in front of the term. If there is already a constant in front of the term, our exponent will be multiplied with it. After we do this, we will lower the exponent by one power.

For the $5x^3$ term:

1) bring the 3 down in front of the term
2) multiply the 3 and the 5 together, getting 15
3) lower the exponent of 3 down to a 2

The derivative of $5x^3$ is $15x^2$

For the $4x^2$ term:

1)   bring the 2 down in front of the term
2)   multiply the 2 and 4 together, getting 8
3)   lower the exponent of 2 down to a 1

The derivative of $4x^2$ is $8x$

For the 7x term, we need to point out a couple of things while using our shortcut. Remember that there is really an exponent of 1 on the x. We just normally do not write in the numeral 1. During the process of applying our shortcut, we always take the exponent and lower it by one power. When we take the exponent of 1 that is on the x and lower it by one power, we will be dropping the exponent on the x to zero. **Remember that anything raised to the zero power is one!** Let's now take the derivative of 7x keeping all of these things in mind.

For the 7x term:

1) bring the exponent of 1 that is on the x down in front of the term
2) multiply the 1 and the 7, getting 7
3) lower the exponent of 1 by one power down to zero
4) since $x^0 = 1$, we get 7 as the derivative

Written out:

The derivative of $7x^1 = 1(7)x^{1-1}$

The derivative of $7x^1 = 1(7)x^0$

The derivative of $7x^1 = 1(7)(1)$

The derivative of $7x^1 = 7$

Lastly, we must take the derivative of our constant term of 3. Remember that the derivative of any constant is zero, meaning that our constant term is again going to disappear in the process of taking the derivative.

Let's put is all together!

The derivative of f(x) = 5x³ + 4x² + 7x + 3 is 15x² + 8x + 7.

Using our notation for derivatives:

$$f'(x) = 15x^2 + 8x + 7$$

If we now wanted to know the slope of the tangent line that touches our original function at some point, all we have to do is insert the point in which we are interested into our derivative.

Example #2

$$f(x) = 6x^4 - 8x^3 + 5x^2 - 2.75$$

Using our shortcut for polynomials to find the derivative:

$$f'(x) = 24x^3 - 24x^2 + 10x$$

There are tow points for this particular example that it is worthwhile to note. First, notice that the second term in the function was a negative $8x^3$. Because the term was negative, we multiplied the exponent of 3 that we brought down by **a negative 8**. Second, even though 2.75 was not an integer it still cancelled in the process of taking the derivative. It does not matter what the number is, **if it is a constant it goes away**.

Example #3

If the tangent line to the function $f(x) = 8x^2 + 9x + 5$ is drawn at x = 1, find the slope of the tangent line.

Remember that when we find the derivative of a function we have found an expression that will give us the slope of the tangent line to the curve at any point in which we are interested. For the function above, the derivative is

$$f'(x) = 16x + 9$$

If we are interested in the slope of the tangent line that can be drawn at x = 1, all we have to do is insert a 1 everywhere that we see an x in the derivative:

$$f'(1) = 16(1) + 9$$
$$f'(1) = 16 + 9$$
$$f'(1) = 25$$

The slope of the tangent line that can be drawn at x = 1 is 25.

Example #4

This last example, before we move on to the next shortcut, is meant to remind us of a couple of properties from algebra.

Find the derivative of the function

$$f(x) = \sqrt[3]{x^2} + \frac{5}{x^2}$$

At first look, it does not appear that we will be able to use our shortcut on this function. We will, in fact, be able to use the shortcut, but we must use a little algebra first. Using algebra, we will rewrite the function in a form that will be conducive to our short. We will look at the two terms in the function separately since they require different rules from algebra.

First, let's look at

$$\sqrt[3]{x^2}$$

Remember that we can always rewrite an expression with a radical using **fractional exponents**. We take the exponent to which the term in the radical is being raised, in our case a 2, and make it the numerator of our fractional exponent. We then take the root that we are calculating, in our case a cube root, and make it the denominator of our fractional exponent. We can think of a cube root as being a "3rd root". This means that we will be using a 3 as the denominator of our fractional exponent. Rewriting our radical expression in terms of fractional exponents:

$$\sqrt[3]{x^2} = x^{\frac{2}{3}}$$

Notice that we are now back to the stage where we have x raised to a power. We will be able to use our shortcut after all!

Now we need to apply algebra to our second term:

$$\frac{5}{x^2}$$

We can always move terms between numerators and denominators of our expressions by changing the sign on the exponent. **We only change the sign on the exponent! We do not change the sign on the whole term!** In our term, the x in the denominator is raised to the 2nd power. We can move it into the numerator of the fraction by changing the 2 to a **negative 2**. When we move it into the numerator of the fraction, it is multiplied by the 5 that is already in the numerator:

$$\frac{5}{x^2} = 5x^{-2}$$

The second term is now also in a form that is appropriate for our shortcut. Let's put our two pieces together and rewrite our original function:

$$f(x) = x^{\frac{2}{3}} + 5x^{-2}$$

> Our shortcut can be used regardless of whether the exponent is a whole number, a fraction, or a negative number. We still follow the same rules involving the lowering of the exponent, etc.

For both terms, bringing down the exponent and lowering the exponent by one power gives us the derivative:

$$f'(x) = \frac{2}{3}x^{-\frac{1}{3}} - 10x^{-3}$$

Now that we have discussed the shortcut for finding the derivative of a simple polynomial, let's move on to another shortcut.

Trick #2 – Functions Involving the Sine and Cosine

Just as in the case of simple polynomials, we could use the formal definition to calculate the derivatives of these functions. The shortcuts for the sine and cosine functions are extremely similar. There is only one small difference for the cosine function. Let's start with the sine function.

Suppose that we have the function

$$f(x) = \sin(3x^2 + 4x)$$

The shortcut for finding the derivative has two steps:

> 1) Take the argument of the sine function (whatever is inside the parentheses) and make it the argument of the cosine function. **Do not change what is inside the parentheses at all!**
> 2) Multiply in front of the cosine function by the derivative of what is inside the parentheses.

Example #5

If we apply our shortcut to our function

$$f(x) = \sin(3x^2 + 4x)$$

The result is

$$f'(x) = (6x + 4)\cos(3x^2 + 4x)$$

Notice, the $(3x^2 + 4x)$ that was inside the sine function in our original function is now inside the cosine function in our derivative (step #1 in our shortcut). Also note, the term in front of the cosine function, $6x + 4$, is the derivative of $(3x^2 + 4x)$, (step #2 in our shortcut).

Example #6

Let's find the derivative of

$$f(x) = 4\sin(6x^3 + 5x^2 - 3x)$$

Since there is a 4 multiplying the function, we will have a 4 multiplying our derivative. Applying our shortcut:

$$f'(x) = 4(18x^2 + 10x - 3)\cos(6x^3 + 5x^2 - 3x)$$

Again, the term in the parentheses of the sine function was placed inside the cosine function without changing it at all, and we multiplied in front of the cosine by the derivative of the term in parentheses.

Our next step is to move on to the cosine function. The shortcut for the cosine function is almost identical to the shortcut for the sine function. There is only one small difference at the end of the shortcut:

1) Take the argument for the cosine function (whatever is inside the parentheses) and make it the argument of the sine function. **Do not change what is inside the parentheses at all!**
2) Multiply in front of the sine function by the derivative of what is inside the parentheses.
3) As a last step, multiply your answer by a negative 1.

Example #7

Suppose that we would like to find the derivative of

$$f(x) = \cos(5x^2 + 6x)$$

Applying our shortcut:

$$f'(x) = -(10x + 6)\sin(5x^2 + 6x)$$

There are three items that should be pointed out at this stage. First, notice that the $(5x^2 + 6x)$ that was inside the cosine function is inside the sine function in our derivative (step #1 in our shortcut). Second, the $(10x + 6)$ that multiplies in front of the sine function is the derivative of $(5x^2 + 6x)$ (step #2 in our shortcut). Third, our final answer was multiplied by a -1, making the derivative negative in this case (step # 3 in our shortcut).

Let's do one more example before we move on to the next shortcut.

Example #8

$$f(x) = -6\cos(4x^3 - 8x^2)$$

Since -6 is multiplying the function, we need to also have a factor of -6 in our derivative. Applying our shortcut:

$$f'(x) = -(-6)(12x^2 - 16x)\sin(4x^3 - 8x^2)$$
$$f'(x) = 6(12x^2 - 16x)\sin(4x^3 - 8x^2)$$

Notice that the negative sign on the 6 and the negative sign inserted due to step #3 of our shortcut cancel one another, leaving our derivative positive in this case.

Although the shortcuts take a little getting used to, you can imagine how difficult these derivatives would be if we calculated them using limits and Δx's!

Trick #3 – Functions Involving the Exponential Function

Before we discuss the shortcut for the exponential function, it would be beneficial for us to review this function. Exponential functions are functions of the sort:

$$f(x) = e^{10x+3}$$

It is worth our time to acquire a very good understanding of this type of function. You will find this particular function in many completely different areas of the world in which we live.

Here are just a couple of the places that the exponential function appears:

1) In an RC-circuit, the equation that will tell us the amount of electric charge on the capacitor during the charging process is

$$q = CV\left(1 - e^{-\frac{t}{RC}}\right)$$

Where q is charge, C is capacitance, V is voltage and t is time.

2) The equation telling us the remaining number of atoms in a radioactive material after a certain amount of time is

$$N = N_0 e^{-\lambda t}$$

Where N is the number remaining after a certain amount of time, N_0 is our initial number of nuclei, λ is the half-life of the particular material and t is time.

The exponential function also appears in population increase/decrease of societies, accounting and many, many other areas. In short, it is a function that we should be very comfortable with if we would like to apply the concepts of differential calculus to it!

At the base of the exponential function is *e*. There are various ways to define *e* but it is most important for our purposes to realize that **_e is an actual number_**. Just like the letter π actually represents a number, 3.14159, the letter *e* also is a shorthand way of writing down a number.

$$e \cong 2.71828$$

You will notice that in the above expression we have used the approximation symbol instead of an actual equal sign. This is because *e* is actually a non-terminating decimal and we are only using the first five decimal places of its value.

Because *e* is an actual number, this means that we are taking this number and raising it to a power in our exponential functions. We just use the letter *e* as a shorthand.

Let's graph two important exponential functions. If we can keep pictures of these two simplest exponential functions in our minds, it gives us great insight how other, more difficult exponential functions behave.

The first of these is $f(x) = e^x$:

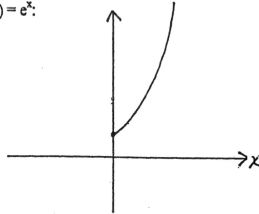

If the exponent on the e is a positive number, the function increases <u>very</u> quickly as we move to the right on the x-axis.

The second of these is $f(x) = e^{-x}$:

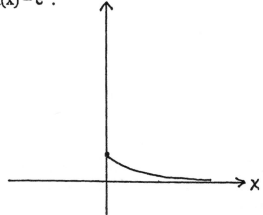

If the exponent on the e is a negative number, the function decreases rapidly as we move to the right on the x-axis. Notice that the function gets closer and closer to the x-axis but never quite touches it.

Now that we understand a little bit about the exponential function it is time to learn our shortcut for calculating its derivative. Just as with our other functions, we are free to use the formal definition to calculate the derivative. This next trick is the shortcut for the exponential function.

1) Recopy the exponential function whose derivative you are trying to calculate **<u>without changing the function at all</u>**.
2) Multiply in front of the function by the derivative of the expression to which the e is raised.

Example #9

Suppose that we would like to find the derivative of

$$f(x) = e^{5x+3}$$

Following our shortcut we first recopy the function, and then multiply in front of it by the derivative of $(5x + 3)$, which is 5:

$$f'(x) = 5e^{5x+3}$$

Just as with the other functions, by calculating the derivative of this particular exponential function, we have found an expression that will give us the slope of the tangent line that can be drawn to the function. If we would like the slope of the tangent line that can be drawn at the point $x = 1$, we simply insert a 1 everywhere that we see an x in our derivative:

$$f'(x) = 5e^{5x+3}$$
$$f'(1) = 5e^{5(1)+3}$$
$$f'(1) = 5e^{8}$$

Remember from earlier in our discussion of the exponential function that e is an actual number. We can take the number that e represents and raise it to the 8th power. Rounding this number to the second decimal place and inserting:

$$f'(1) = 5(2980.96)$$
$$f'(1) = 14904.8$$

We will do one more example involving the exponential function and then it's on to our next shortcut!

Example #10

Find the derivative of the function

$$f(x) = 4e^{6x-10}$$

Notice that because there is a 4 multiplying the function, we will have a factor of 4 multiplying our derivative. Applying our shortcut:

$$f'(x) = 4(6)e^{6x-10}$$
$$f'(x) = 24e^{6x-10}$$

It might be helpful at this stage to pause for a moment and summarize what we have done so far in this chapter. We have learned the shortcuts for how to calculate the derivatives of a few simple types of functions, namely:

1) simply polynomials
2) sine and cosine functions
3) exponential functions

We realize that we can always resort to the formal definition to calculate our derivatives. These shortcuts provide us with a much faster and easier way to calculate the derivatives of functions. This is of great help to us since our eventual goal is to be able to apply the concept of the derivative to physical problems.

In this section, we discussed how to find the derivatives of some simple types of functions. In the next section, we move on to functions that are combinations of these simple types. We will be discussing the shortcuts that can be used on these combinations.

As we begin to cover the combinations of the functions that have been discussed in the previous sections, it is important to realize that we are again learning shortcuts. For all of the combinations below, **we could still use the formal definition to find the derivative.**

Trick #4 – The Product Rule

When we first learned basic algebra, the term <u>product</u> meant multiplication – **it still does!** We use the shortcut known as **the product rule** whenever we have two expressions multiplied together, such as

$$f(x) = (3x^2 + 4x + 8)(7x^3 + 5x^2)$$

To find the derivative of this type of function:

Take the first times the derivative of the second, plus the second times the derivative of the first.

Example #11

For the function above, the first term is $(3x^2 + 4x + 8)$ and the second term is $(7x^3 + 5x^2)$. The product rule is a step-by-step recipe for finding the derivative. We are supposed to write down the first term and multiply it by the derivative of the second term. After we do this, we are supposed to add on the second term multiplied by the derivative of the first term. Applying the product rule to our example function:

$$f'(x) = (3x^2 + 4x + 8)(21x^2 + 10x) + (7x^3 + 5x^2)(6x + 4)$$

Example #12

Let's do another example using simple polynomials and then move on to a little harder one. For the function:

$$f(x) = (5x^4 - 3x^2)(8x^6 + 4x^5 + 2x^3)$$

Our first term is $(5x^4 - 3x^2)$ and our second term is $(8x^6 + 4x^5 + 2x^3)$. Applying the product rule:

$$f'(x) = (5x^4 - 3x^2)(48x^5 + 20x^4 + 6x^2) + (8x^6 + 4x^5 + 2x^3)(20x^3 - 6x)$$

The product rule can be used whenever we have two terms multiplied together, not just if the two terms are simple polynomials. Let's do another example. In the following example, one of the terms is not a simple polynomial. Yet, we apply the product rule the same way. We take the first times the derivative of the second plus the second times the derivative of the first.

Example #13

Find the derivative of

$$f(x) = e^{5x+3}(2x^3 + 4x)$$

In this function e $^{5x+3}$ is the first term and $(2x^3 + 4x)$ is the second term. Using our product rule as a step-by-step recipe:

$$f'(x) = e^{5x+3}(6x^2 + 4) + (2x^3 + 4x)(5e^{5x+3})$$

Although our shortcuts, like the product rule, take a little while to learn and apply, they are definitely easier than using the formal definition!

Now that we have learned the shortcut for two expressions multiplied together, let's discuss the shortcut if we have two functions divided by one another.

Trick #5 – The Quotient Rule

Like the product rule, the quotient rule is a step-by-step recipe that allows us to find the derivative of a function such as

$$f(x) = \frac{4x^3 + 3x^2 - 7x}{5x^2 + 4x}$$

To find the derivative of this type of function:

> Take the denominator times the derivative of the numerator <u>minus</u> the numerator times the derivative of the denominator <u>all</u> over the denominator squared.

Example #14

Let's use our shortcut to find the derivative of the function given above. Remember that the numerator is the top of the fraction and the denominator is the bottom of the fraction. In the recipe you will note that the word "all" has been stressed. This is meant to emphasize the fact that once we do the first portion of the recipe involving derivatives of numerators, etc., we are to place all of it over the denominator of the original function original function squared. Applying the shortcut:

$$f'(x) = \frac{(5x^2 + 4x)(12x^2 + 6x - 7) - (4x^3 + 3x^2 - 7x)(10x + 4)}{(5x^2 + 4x)^2}$$

It's a little long, but it is definitely simpler than trying to use the formal definition!

Example #15

The shortcut called the quotient rule may be used anytime that you have one expression divided by another, **not** just if the expressions are simple polynomials.

Find the derivative of

$$f(x) = \frac{\sin(2x)}{\cos(3x)}$$

In this example, sin(2x) is the numerator and cos(3x) is the denominator. Applying our shortcut:

$$f'(x) = \frac{(\cos 3x)(2\cos 2x) - (\sin 2x)(-\sin 3x)}{(\cos 3x)^2}$$

Our last type of function in this chapter involves expressions that have been raised to a power.

Trick #6 – The Power Rule

The shortcut known as the power rule is used on functions of the type:

$$f(x) = (3x^2 + 5x)^5$$

Finding the derivative of this type of function is a two-step process:

1) Take the exponent that is on the expression, bring it down in front of the parentheses, and lower the exponent by one power. **Do not change what is inside the parentheses!**
2) Multiply the term in step 1) by the derivative of what is inside the parentheses.

Example #16

  Let's use our shortcut on the function written above. First, we bring the 5 down and place it as a coefficient in front of the parentheses. Next, we rewrite our term in parentheses to one lower power (in this case 4). Lastly, we multiply by the derivative of what is inside the parentheses, in this case (6x + 5):

$$f'(x) = 5(3x^2 + 5x)^4(6x + 5)$$

  Remember, just as with our other shortcuts, we could have applied the formal definition to our function and it would have worked. The power rule is just a shortcut.

Example #17

  Find the derivative of

$$f(x) = (7x^3 - 6x^2 + 3x)^8$$

Applying our shortcut:

$$f'(x) = 8(7x^3 - 6x^2 + 3x)^7(21x^2 - 12x + 3)$$

Exercises

Find the derivative of the following functions:

Section I

1. $f(x) = 6x^2 + 4x + 3$

2. $f(x) = 5x - 4$

3. $f(x) = 7x^5 - 2x^4$

4. $f(x) = 8x^2 + 15$

5. $f(x) = 2x - 5x^3$

6. $f(x) = -4x + 19$

7. $f(x) = 14x^2 + 7x - 6.75$

8. $f(x) = 8.3x + 7$

9. $f(x) = 9$

10. $f(x) = 12x - 4.3x^2 + 5x^4$

Section II

The problems in this section are a little more difficult and may require some algebra!

11.

$$f(x) = \frac{3}{x^2}$$

12.

$$f(x) = \sqrt[3]{x^4}$$

13.

$$f(x) = \sqrt{x}$$

14.

$$f(x) = x^3 + \sqrt{x}$$

15.

$$f(x) = \frac{4}{\sqrt[3]{x}}$$

16.

$$f(x) = 4x^3 - 5x^2 + \frac{7}{x} + 3$$

17.

$$f(x) = \frac{x^2 - 4}{x - 2}$$

18.

$$f(x) = \frac{4}{x^5} + \frac{3}{x^2} + 5$$

19.

$$f(x) = \frac{3x^2 + 4x}{x}$$

20.

$$f(x) = \frac{x^3}{\sqrt{x}}$$

SOLUTIONS

Section I

1. $12x + 4$

2. 5

3. $35x^4 - 8x^3$

4. $16x$

5. $2 - 15x^2$

6. -4

7. $28x + 7$

8. 8.3

9. 0

10. $12 - 8.6x + 20x^3$

Section II

11. The first step in solving this problem is to rewrite the function with x^2 in the numerator. To do this, we must change the 2 to a -2:

$$f(x) = 3x^{-2}$$

Now we can bring down the exponent, multiply it be the 3, and lower our exponent by one power:

$$f'(x) = -6x^{-3}$$

12. The trick here is to first rewrite the function in terms of a fractional exponent before we try to take the derivative of the function:

$$f(x) = \sqrt[3]{x^4} = x^{\frac{4}{3}}$$

Now, we can find the derivative of the function using our shortcut for simple polynomials:

$$f'(x) = \frac{4}{3}x^{\frac{1}{3}}$$

13. Just as with problem 12, we first rewrite the function using fractional exponents. The square root is a little tricky for some students at first. Remember that there is really an exponent of 1 on the x, and that we can think of the square root as the "2nd" root:

$$f(x) = \sqrt{x} = x^{\frac{1}{2}}$$

Calculating the derivative:

$$f'(x) = \frac{1}{2}x^{-\frac{1}{2}}$$

14. This problem is similar to problem 13, except for the additional term of x^3. As before, our first step is to remove the radical using fractional exponents:

$$f(x) = x^3 + x^{\frac{1}{2}}$$

Calculating the derivative:

$$f'(x) = 3x^2 + \frac{1}{2}x^{-\frac{1}{2}}$$

15. There are two steps of algebra that we need to do in order to put our function into a form that is more conducive to finding the derivative. First, we want to remove the radical by using fractional exponents:

$$f(x) = \frac{4}{\sqrt[3]{x}} = \frac{4}{x^{\frac{1}{3}}}$$

Next, we can move the denominator to the numerator by changing the sign on the exponent:

$$f(x) = \frac{4}{x^{\frac{1}{3}}} = 4x^{-\frac{1}{3}}$$

Our function is now in a form from which we can calculate the derivative:

$$f'(x) = \left(-\frac{1}{3}\right)(4)x^{-\frac{4}{3}} = -\frac{4}{3}x^{-\frac{4}{3}}$$

16. The third term in the expression needs to be rewritten so that we can easily find the derivative. We can do this by moving the x from the denominator to the numerator:

$$f(x) = 4x^3 - 5x^2 + 7x^{-1} + 3$$

Calculating the derivative:

$$f'(x) = 12x^2 - 10x - 7x^{-2}$$

17.   At first glance, this function appears to be out of range for the use of our shortcut. The key here is to realize that the numerator of the expression can be factored since it is the difference of two squares:

$$f(x) = \frac{x^2 - 4}{x - 2} = \frac{(x-2)(x+2)}{x-2}$$

Canceling the factor of $(x - 2)$ between the numerator and the denominator gives us a form of our original function f(x) that is easily differentiable:

$$f(x) = x + 2$$

Finding the derivative of our function:

$$f'(x) = 1$$

18.   First we rewrite our function with the denominators of the first two terms raised to the numerator:

$$f(x) = 4x^{-5} + 3x^{-2} + 5$$

Calculating the derivative:

$$f'(x) = -20x^{-6} - 6x^{-3}$$

19.   Since both terms in the numerator of the expression have an x, we can factor it out:

$$f(x) = \frac{x(3x + 4)}{x}$$

Canceling the factor of x between the numerator and the denominator:

$$f(x) = 3x + 4$$

Finding the derivative of the function:

$$f'(x) = 3$$

20. First, we remove the radical in the expression, replacing it with a fractional exponent:

$$f(x) = \frac{x^3}{x^{\frac{1}{2}}}$$

Since we have the same variable in both the numerator and the denominator, we can simplify the expression by subtracting the bottom exponent from the top exponent:

$$f(x) = x^{\frac{5}{2}}$$

Now we can find the derivative of our function:

$$f'(x) = \frac{5}{2}x^{\frac{3}{2}}$$

Exercises

Find the derivative of the following functions involving the sine, cosine and exponential function:

Section I

1. $f(x) = \sin(x^2 + 4x)$

2. $f(x) = \sin(3x - 1)$

3. $f(x) = \cos(5x + 6)$

4. $f(x) = \cos(7x^3 + 5x^2)$

5. $f(x) = e^{6x-1}$

6. $f(x) = e^{5x+2}$

7. $f(x) = \sin(8x^4 + 7x^3)$

8. $f(x) = \cos(9x^2 - 10x - 11)$

9. $f(x) = e^{3.4x}$

10. $f(x) = \sin(4x) + \cos(3x)$

Section II

This section is meant to reinforce the derivatives of the sine, cosine, and exponential function, while reminding the student of how to calculate the derivative of simple polynomials.

Find the derivative of the following functions:

11.

$$f(x) = \sin(3x-1) + 5x^2$$

12.

$$f(x) = e^{5x^2+4x} + 15x - 12$$

13.

$$f(x) = \sin(4x^5 - 6x^3 + 3x) + e^{8x^4 + 9x^2}$$

14.

$$f(x) = \sqrt{x} + \cos(7x + 12)$$

15.

$$f(x) = e^{7.5x+3} + \cos(4x^8) + \frac{4}{x^3}$$

16.

$$f(x) = \sqrt{x^3} + \frac{6}{x^5} + \sin(7x^3 + 2x - 8)$$

17.

$$f(x) = e^{-7x} + 8x + 9x^2 + \cos(12x^2)$$

18.

$$f(x) = \frac{1}{4}x^3 + \frac{2}{5}e^{6x^4 - 3x}$$

Section III

The last two problems in this exercise set are meant to reinforce a couple of the algebraic concepts that are important for us as we continue in our discussion of calculus.

Find the derivative of the following functions:

19.   Hint: Remember that you can move a term from the denominator to the numerator by changing the sign on the exponent!

$$f(x) = \frac{4}{e^{3x^2+6x}}$$

20.   Hint: Look for the like factors and make the expression as simple as possible before trying to find the derivative of the function.

$$f(x) = \frac{3x^2 - x^2 \sin(5x^3)}{x^2}$$

SOLUTIONS

Section I

1. $(2x+4)\cos(x^2+4x)$

2. $3\cos(3x-1)$

3. $-5\sin(5x+6)$

4. $-(21x^2+10x)\sin(7x^3+5x^2)$

5. $6e^{6x-1}$

6. $5e^{5x+2}$

7. $(32x^3+21x^2)\cos(8x^4+7x^3)$

8. $-(18x-10)\sin(9x^2-10x-11)$

9. $3.4e^{3.4x}$

10. $4\cos(4x)-3\sin(3x)$

Section II

11. This function marries a shortcut from this section with a shortcut from a previous section. All we have to do is treat the two terms separately using the appropriate shortcut for each term:

$$f'(x)=3\cos(3x-1)+10x$$

12. The first term requires us to use the shortcut for the exponential function, while the other two use the shortcuts from the previous section on simple polynomials:

$$f'(x)=(10x+4)e^{5x^2+4x}+15$$

13. This problem requires us to use the shortcut for the sine function and the shortcut for the exponential function. We deal with each term separately using the appropriate shortcut for each term:

$$f'(x)=(20x^4-18x^2+3)\cos(4x^5-6x^3+3x)+(32x^3+18x)e^{8x^4+9x^2}$$

84

14. Our first step is to replace the radical with a fractional exponent. This replacement will put our function into a form where we can deal with each of the two terms using the appropriate shortcut:

$$f(x) = x^{\frac{1}{2}} + \cos(7x+12)$$

Now we find the derivative of each of the terms separately:

$$f'(x) = \frac{1}{2}x^{-\frac{1}{2}} - 7\sin(7x+12)$$

15. We will be able to treat each of the three terms separately once we put the third term into the appropriate form. We can do this by moving the term in the denominator into the numerator:

$$f(x) = e^{7.5x+3} + \cos(4x^8) + 4x^{-3}$$

Now finding the derivative of each of the terms:

$$f'(x) = 7.5e^{7.5x+3} - 32x^7 \sin(4x^8) - 12x^{-4}$$

16. To find the derivative of our function, we must rewrite the first two terms using the rules from algebra that we've used before:

$$f(x) = x^{\frac{3}{2}} + 6x^{-5} + \sin(7x^3 + 2x - 8)$$

Now finding the derivative of each of the terms, one at a time:

$$f'(x) = \frac{3}{2}x^{\frac{1}{2}} - 30x^{-6} + (21x^2 + 2)\cos(7x^3 + 2x - 8)$$

17. Each of the terms in the function are already in a form to use our shortcuts. To find the derivative, we just treat each of our terms one at a time:

$$f'(x) = -7e^{-7x} + 8 + 18x - 24x\sin(12x^2)$$

18. No algebra is required for this one!

$$f'(x) = \frac{3}{4}x^2 + \frac{2}{5}\left(24x^3 - 3\right)e^{6x^4 - 3x}$$

Section III

19. Our trick of moving terms between denominators and numerators can still be used for this function. We have a term raised to a power. All we have to do to move this term to the numerator of the expression is to change the sign on the exponent:

$$f(x) = \frac{4}{e^{3x^2 + 6x}} = 4e^{-(3x^2 + 6x)} = 4e^{-3x^2 - 6x}$$

Now we can find the derivative of the function using our shortcut for the exponential function:

$$f'(x) = 4(-6x - 6)e^{-3x^2 - 6x}$$

20. Notice that each of the terms in the numerator has an x^2. We can factor it out front in the numerator and then cancel it with the x^2 in the denominator:

$$f(x) = \frac{3x^2 - x^2\sin(5x^3)}{x^2} = \frac{x^2\left[3 - \sin(5x^3)\right]}{x^2}$$

$$f(x) = 3 - \sin(5x^3)$$

Calculating the derivative of the function:

$$f'(x) = -15x^2\cos(5x^3)$$

Exercises

<u>Section I</u>

Use the product rule, quotient rule, or power rule to find the derivative of these functions involving simple polynomials:

1.

$$f(x) = (3x^2 + 8x)(5x^3 + 7x^2 - 6x)$$

2.

$$f(x) = (4x^5 + 5x^2 + 3x)(9x^2 - 6x)$$

3.

$$f(x) = \frac{x^3 + 4x^2}{7x^4 + 3x^3}$$

4.

$$f(x) = \frac{9x - 1}{x^5 - 6x^3}$$

5.

$$f(x) = (4x^3 + 5x^2 - 6x)^4$$

6.

$$f(x) = (7x^2 - 11x + 10)^6$$

7.

$$f(x) = (6x^3 + 5x)(4x^4 - 7x^2)$$

8.

$$f(x) = (5x^7 - 6x^4 + 9x^2)^5$$

9.

$$f(x) = \frac{5x^4 + 3x^2 - 9x}{4x^2 - 7.5x + 3.2}$$

10.

$$f(x) = (5x^3 + 7x)^4 + \frac{3x^3 - 4x^2}{9x^2 - 8x + 2}$$

Section II

Use the product rule, quotient rule, or the power rule to find the derivative of these functions involving a mixture of the sine function, the cosine function, the exponential function and simple polynomials.

Remember that the product rule, the quotient rule and the power rule have not changed even though the functions are of different types.

11.

$$f(x) = \frac{e^{4x^3 + 6x^2}}{3x^4}$$

12.

$$f(x) = (7x^2 - 6x + 9)\sin(5x^3 + 8x)$$

13.

$$f(x) = (5x + e^{7x})^4$$

14.

$$f(x) = \frac{\sin(4x - 2)}{\sqrt{x^5}}$$

15.

$$f(x) = (6x + \sqrt{x})(5x^3 + 8x^2 - 12x)$$

16.

$$f(x) = \frac{\cos(5x^2 - 6x)}{\sin(8x^3)}$$

17.

$$f(x) = \frac{4}{\sqrt[3]{x^7}} + \frac{e^{9x}}{x^2 + 3x}$$

The last three problems in this section are slightly more challenging. A hint has been included for each one.

18. Hint: Remember that you can remove the radical symbol by rewriting the expression inside the radical with a fractional exponent.

$$f(x) = \sqrt{4x^3 - 7x^2}$$

19. Hint: Remember how to factor the difference two cubes. Simplify the expression as much as possible before trying to find the derivative.

$$f(x) = \frac{(x^3 - 8)\sin(9x^2 + 5x)}{x - 2}$$

20. Hint: Remember that e is a number!!

$$f(x) = e^2(6x^3 + 5x)\cos(7x)$$

SOLUTIONS

Product Rule: The first times the derivative of the second plus the second times the derivative of the first.

Quotient Rule: The denominator times the derivative of the numerator minus the numerator times the derivative of the denominator all over the denominator squared.

Power Rule: Take the exponent that is on the parentheses, bring it down and make it a coefficient. Lower the original exponent by one power. Multiply by the derivative of what is inside the parentheses.

The solutions in this section have intentionally been left unsimplified so that the students can see whether or not they have executed the rules correctly

1.   The product rule should be used for this function. The first term is $3x^2 + 8x$ and the second term is $5x^3 + 7x^2 - 6x$:

$$f'(x) = (3x^2 + 8x)(15x^2 + 14x - 6) + (5x^3 + 7x^2 - 6x)(6x + 8)$$

2.   Once again using our product rule:

$$f'(x) = (4x^5 + 5x^2 + 3x)(18x - 6) + (9x^2 - 6x)(20x^4 + 10x + 3)$$

3.   Since we have one expression divided by another expression, we want to use the quotient rule to find the derivative of this function. Remember that the numerator is the term on the top of the fraction and the denominator is the term on the bottom of the fraction:

$$f'(x) = \frac{(7x^4 + 3x^3)(3x^2 + 8x) - (x^3 + 4x^2)(28x^3 + 9x^2)}{(7x^4 + 3x^3)^2}$$

4.   As in exercise 3, since we have one expression divided by another expression, we need to use the quotient rule to find the derivative of the function:

$$f'(x) = \frac{(x^5 - 6x^3)(9) - (9x - 1)(5x^4 - 18x^2)}{(x^5 - 6x^3)^2}$$

5. Since we have an entire expression raised to a power, we want to use the power rule here to find the derivative:

$$f'(x) = 4(4x^3 + 5x^2 - 6x)^3 (12x^2 + 10x - 6)$$

6. Again, we have an expression raised to a power which means that we need the power rule to find the derivative of this function:

$$f'(x) = 6(7x^2 - 11x + 10)^5 (14x - 11)$$

7. Since we have two expressions multiplied together, we use the product rule to find the derivative of this function:

$$f'(x) = (6x^3 + 5x)(16x^3 - 14x) + (4x^4 - 7x^2)(18x^2 + 5)$$

8. Using the power rule:

$$f'(x) = 5(5x^7 - 6x^4 + 9x^2)^4 (35x^6 - 24x^3 + 18x)$$

9. Using the quotient rule to find the derivative:

$$f'(x) = \frac{(4x^2 - 7.5x + 3.2)(20x^3 + 6x - 9) - (5x^4 + 3x^2 - 9x)(8x - 7.5)}{(4x^2 - 7.5x + 3.2)^2}$$

10. This problem involves using two of our shortcuts. Since the first term is an expression raised to a power, we will use the power rule to find its derivative. For the second term, since it is one expression divided by another expression, we will use the quotient rule. Since the two terms are simply added together, we can address them separately:

$$f'(x) = 4(5x^3 + 7x)^3 (15x^2 + 7) + \frac{(9x^2 - 8x + 2)(9x^2 - 8x) - (3x^3 - 4x^2)(18x - 8))}{(9x^2 - 8x + 2)^2}$$

11. The key to this problem is to again realize that we have one expression divided by another expression. Because of this, we want to use the quotient rule to find the

derivative. The area in which we need to be slightly more careful, this time, is the term in the quotient rule where we are asked for the derivative of the numerator. Remember that to find the derivative of the numerator, we will need to use the shortcut for the exponential function. Employing the quotient rule:

$$f'(x) = \frac{3x^4(12x^2 + 12x)e^{4x^3+6x^2} - e^{4x^3+6x^2}(12x^3)}{(3x^4)^2}$$

12. Since we have two terms multiplied together, we will use the product rule to find the derivative of this function. In this case our first term is $7x^2 - 6x + 9$ and our second term is $\sin(5x^3 + 8x)$:

$$f'(x) = (7x^2 - 6x + 9)(15x^2 + 8)\cos(5x^3 + 8x) + \left[\sin(5x^3 + 8x)\right](14x - 6)$$

13. The power rule is to be used here since we have an entire expression raised to a power. Remember that we will need to find the derivative of the exponential function in the process of using the power rule since we must multiply by the derivative of what is inside of the parentheses:

$$f'(x) = 4(5x + e^{7x})^3(5 + 7e^{7x})$$

14. Since we have two terms divided by one another, we will be using the quotient rule. Before we do this, however, we want to rewrite the denominator using a fractional exponent:

$$f(x) = \frac{\sin(4x - 2)}{x^{\frac{5}{2}}}$$

Now using the quotient rule to find the derivative:

$$f'(x) = \frac{x^{\frac{5}{2}}[4\cos(4x-2)] - [\sin(4x-2)]\left(\frac{5}{2}x^{\frac{3}{2}}\right)}{\left(x^{\frac{5}{2}}\right)^2}$$

Again, the above equation could be simplified. It is being left in this form so that students can make sure that they have executed the quotient rule correctly.

15.   Before employing the product rule to find the derivative of this function, we need to rewrite the term with the radical using a fractional exponent:

$$f(x) = (6x + x^{\frac{1}{2}})(5x^3 + 8x^2 - 12x)$$

Now we can use our product rule to find the derivative of the function:

$$f'(x) = (6x + x^{\frac{1}{2}})(15x^2 + 16x - 12) + (5x^3 + 8x^2 - 12x)(6 + \frac{1}{2}x^{-\frac{1}{2}})$$

16.   Following the quotient rule:

$$f'(x) = \frac{[\sin(8x^3)][-(10x-6)\sin(5x^2-6x)] - [\cos(5x^2-6x)][24x^2\cos(8x^3)]}{[\sin(8x^3)]^2}$$

17. Our first step is to rewrite the denominator of the first term using a fractional exponent and then to move it to the numerator by changing the sign on the exponent:

$$f(x) = 4x^{-\frac{7}{3}} + \frac{e^{9x}}{x^2 + 3x}$$

Now we can find the derivative of the function by addressing each term separately. We will need to use the quotient rule to find the derivative of the second term in the function:

$$f'(x) = 4(-\frac{7}{3}x^{-\frac{10}{3}}) + \frac{(x^2 + 3x)(9e^{9x}) - e^{9x}(2x+3)}{(x^2 + 3x)^2}$$

18. Since the entire expression is inside of the radical, we can rewrite the function using fractional exponents:

$$f(x) = (4x^3 - 7x^2)^{\frac{1}{2}}$$

Now that we've done this, we can use the power rule to find the derivative of the function:

$$f'(x) = \frac{1}{2}(4x^3 - 7x^2)^{-\frac{1}{2}}(12x^2 - 14x)$$

19. The hint that was given in the problem was to factor the difference of two cubes. Remember that $x^3 - 8$ factors into:

$$x^3 - 8 = x^3 - 2^3 = (x-2)(x^2 + 2x + 4)$$

If we insert this into our function:

$$f(x) = \frac{(x-2)(x^2 + 2x + 4)\sin(9x^2 + 5x)}{x - 2}$$

The factor of $x - 2$ cancels between the numerator and the denominator, leaving:

$$f(x) = (x^2 + 2x + 4)\sin(9x^2 + 5x)$$

Our function is now in a form to use the product rule to find the derivative:

$$f'(x) = (x^2 + 2x + 4)(18x + 5)\cos(9x^2 + 5x) + \left[\sin(9x^2 + 5x)\right](2x + 2)$$

20. At first glance it might appear that there are three terms for us to deal with in this problem. If you notice, however, the e has been raised to a number **not** to a variable. Remember that e is a number, which means that e^2 is just going to be a coefficient that will multiply our final answer.

We are, therefore, left with:

$$f(x) = e^2(6x^3 + 5x)\cos(7x)$$

Using the product rule and remembering to multiply our answer by the e^2 that is in the front of our function:

$$f'(x) = e^2\left[(6x^3 + 5x)(-7\sin(7x)) + \cos(7x)(18x^2 + 5)\right]$$

Exercises

The purpose of this set of exercises is to bring together all of the shortcuts that have been developed in the preceding sections.

Find the derivative of each of the following functions:

1.

$$f(x) = 7x^3 - 5x$$

2.

$$f(x) = (3x - 5)^7$$

3.

$$f(x) = \sin(9x^3 - 4x)$$

4.

$$f(x) = \frac{3x^4 - 7x^2}{4x - 3}$$

5.

$$f(x) = e^{4x^2 - 5x + 2}$$

6.

$$f(x) = \sqrt{2x + 5}$$

7.

$$f(x) = \frac{5}{x^4} + \cos(4x)$$

8.

$$f(x) = (6x^2 - 4x)(5x^3 + 7x - 3)$$

9.

$$f(x) = 8x^4 - 6x^3 + 3x$$

10.

$$f(x) = \frac{e^{3x}}{2x - 7}$$

11.

$$f(x) = \frac{9}{\sqrt[3]{x}}$$

12.

$$f(x) = e^{5x}(4x^2 - 11x)$$

13.

$$f(x) = \sin(5x) + \frac{4x - 12}{x^2 + 2x}$$

14.

$$f(x) = \frac{\cos(8x+2)}{\sqrt{x}}$$

15.

$$f(x) = \sqrt[3]{9x^2 + 5x - 6}$$

16.

$$f(x) = \frac{5}{e^{6x^2 + 2x}}$$

17.

$$f(x) = (9x^4 + 5x)^6 + \sin(10x)$$

18.

$$f(x) = \frac{(3x+2)(5x^3 - 9x^2 + 8x)}{4}$$

19.

$$f(x) = e^{4x^3} + (5x^2 + 14x)^7 + \cos(3x)$$

20.

$$f(x) = \sqrt{e^{3x} + \sin(2x^3)}$$

SOLUTIONS

1.

$$f'(x) = 21x^2 - 5$$

2.

$$f'(x) = 7(3x - 5)^6 (3)$$

3.

$$f'(x) = (27x^2 - 4)\cos(9x^3 - 4x)$$

4.

$$f'(x) = \frac{(4x - 3)(12x^3 - 14x) - (3x^4 - 7x^2)(4)}{(4x - 3)^2}$$

5.

$$f'(x) = (8x - 5)e^{4x^2 - 5x + 2}$$

6.

$$f'(x) = \frac{1}{2}(2x + 5)^{-\frac{1}{2}}(2)$$

7.

$$f'(x) = -20x^{-5} - 4\sin(4x)$$

8.

$$f'(x) = (6x^2 - 4x)(15x^2 + 7) + (5x^3 + 7x - 3)(12x - 4)$$

9.

$$f'(x) = 32x^3 - 18x^2 + 3$$

10.

$$f'(x) = \frac{(2x-7)(3e^{3x}) - e^{3x}(2)}{(2x-7)^2}$$

11.

$$f'(x) = -3x^{-\frac{4}{3}}$$

12.

$$f'(x) = e^{5x}(8x-11) + (4x^2 - 11x)(5e^{5x})$$

13.

$$f'(x) = 5\cos(5x) + \frac{(x^2+2x)(4) - (4x-12)(2x+2)}{(x^2+2x)^2}$$

14.

$$f'(x) = \frac{x^{\frac{1}{2}}\left[-8\sin(8x+2)\right] - \cos(8x+2)\left(\frac{1}{2}x^{-\frac{1}{2}}\right)}{\left(x^{\frac{1}{2}}\right)^2}$$

It is also possible to move the denominator of the fraction into the numerator before finding the derivative. If this is done, the product rule is used, yielding:

$$f'(x) = x^{-\frac{1}{2}}\left[-8\sin(8x+2)\right] + \cos(8x+2)\left(-\frac{1}{2}\right)x^{-\frac{3}{2}}$$

15.

$$f'(x) = \frac{1}{3}(9x^2 + 5x - 6)^{-\frac{2}{3}}(18x+5)$$

16.

$$f'(x) = 5(-12x - 2)e^{-6x^2 - 2x}$$

17.

$$f'(x) = 6(9x^4 + 5x)^5(36x^3 + 5) + 10\cos(10x)$$

18.

$$f'(x) = \frac{1}{4}\left[(3x+2)(15x^2 - 18x + 8) + (5x^3 - 9x^2 + 8x)(3)\right]$$

19.

$$f'(x) = 12x^2 e^{4x^3} + 7(5x^2 + 14x)^6(10x + 14) - 3\sin(3x)$$

20.

$$f'(x) = \frac{1}{2}\left(e^{3x} + \sin(2x^3)\right)^{-\frac{1}{2}}\left(3e^{3x} + 6x^2\cos(2x^3)\right)$$

CHAPTER 4

HIGHER ORDER DERIVATIVES AND PHYSICAL APPLICATIONS OF THE DERIVATIVE

An Alternative Way to Write Derivatives – Differentials

In this chapter, we are going to learn a way of expressing derivatives that will be extremely useful to us as we begin applying the methods of differential calculus to physical problems. <u>We will still be calculating our derivatives using the shortcuts that were covered in the previous sections.</u>

From a previous chapter, we discussed the fact that we can express the slope of a line as

$$slope = \frac{\Delta y}{\Delta x}$$

and that this slope can be interpreted as the rate at which y is changing if we change x. <u>Differentials</u> are directly related to the idea that slopes are rates of change. Suppose that we have the following generic function with a typical tangent line drawn at a point on the function:

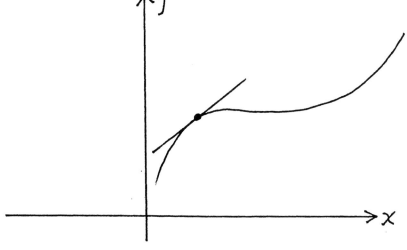

The slope of this tangent line, as we have mentioned many times before, is the same as the derivative of the function at that point. We can apply the idea that the slope of this tangent line is the rate of change of our dependent variable with respect to our independent variable.

The slope of this tangent line is the rate at which y is changing with respect to x as that point.

Now it is time to use the concept of a <u>differential</u>. Differentials are infinitely small amounts of change in a certain quantity. Since the Greek letter delta (Δ) is used for change, we use the letter d to represent our infinitely small amount of change (d is the first letter of delta.

For example, Δx is how we would write down the amount of distance that we moved along the x-axis. If we wanted to express an infinitely small amount of movement along the x-axis, we would write

$$dx$$

If, as another example, we wanted to express the amount that the velocity of a certain object changed, we would write Δv. If the object's velocity changed by an infinitely small amount, we would write

$$dv$$

Now that we understand a little bit about differentials, let's apply these ideas to our slopes. Again looking at our function with its tangent line:

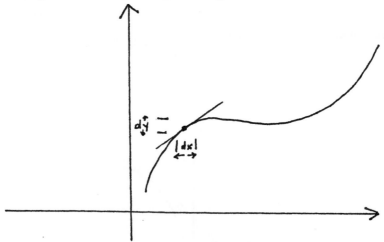

We can express the slope of the line in terms of differentials. The slope of this tangent line is the rate at which y is changing, <u>at our point of interest</u>, with respect to x. In other words, the rate at which y is changing if we move an infinitely small distance along the x-axis.

> If we move an infinitely small distance along the x-axis, we will get an infinitely small change in y.

Since we know that we can express the slope of a line as

$$slope = \frac{\Delta y}{\Delta x}$$

and we also know that we are dealing with an infinitesimal change along the y-axis (dy) as we move an infinitesimal distance along the x-axis (dx), we can express the slope of our tangent line at our point of interest as:

$$slope = \frac{dy}{dx}$$

We can write out the relationship between our original slope equation involving Δ's and our new one involving d's using the language of limits:

$$slope = \lim_{\Delta x \to 0} \frac{\Delta y}{\Delta x} = \frac{dy}{dx}$$

At this point, you are probably asking yourself why we are bothering to go through all of this right in the middle of trying to learn how to find the derivatives of functions. We can merge the ideas of derivatives with the ideas of differentials and arrive at a way of writing down our derivatives that will be very useful to us when we begin applying our derivatives to physical problems.

We know that we can find the derivative of the following function using our shortcuts:

$$f(x) = 3x^2 + 4x$$
$$f'(x) = 6x + 4$$

Suppose that instead of writing down our function and calling it f(x) we write it down and return to calling it y:

$$y = 3x^2 + 4x$$

Since the slope of the tangent line and the derivative are the same thing, our language of differentials gives us another way of writing down derivatives:

$$\frac{dy}{dx} = 6x + 4$$

This way of writing down derivatives is convenient for two reasons. First, it emphasizes the fact that derivatives and slopes are really the same thing. Second, and this is the point at which we will get the payoff as we apply it to physical problems, it explicitly states that the dependent variable is changing with respect to the independent variable. In our example, y is changing with respect to x.

It is extremely important to note at this point:

> We have not changed the shortcuts that we use to calculate our derivatives. This is simply an additional way to write down our derivatives!

Let's do two more examples. These examples will allow us to reinforce a couple of our shortcuts, also further acquaints us with the concept of differentials.

Example #1

Suppose that our function is given by

$$y = (4x^3 + 5x^2)^5$$

Using the power rule and expressing the derivative in our new language of differentials:

$$\frac{dy}{dx} = 5(4x^3 + 5x^2)^4(12x^2 + 10x)$$

Example #2

In this example, let's start with a function that has a different dependent variable and independent variable. As we begin to apply the concepts of differential calculus to physical problems, it is important for us to realize that we may have different dependent and independent variables than simply y and x.

Suppose that our function is

$$B = e^{6t+4}$$

In this case, B is our dependent variable and t is our independent variable. Applying the exponential rule and again expressing our derivative in the language of differentials:

$$\frac{dB}{dt} = 6e^{6t+4}$$

To summarize, there are times when our functions will be written using functional notation (using f(x)) and there will be times when our functions will be written in terms of y's, etc. The manner in which we write the derivative changes (f'(x), dy/dx) but not the shortcuts that we use to calculate the derivatives. When we find the derivative of a function we are still finding the slope of the tangent line to the curve and the rate at which the dependent variable is changing with respect to the independent variable at that point.

Higher Order Derivatives

In this section we discuss the idea of finding higher order derivatives. The concept is not difficult. We will still be using all of the shortcuts that have been previously developed.

Higher order derivatives involves finding the derivative of the same function more than one time.

Suppose that we have the function

$$f(x) = 3x^4 + 2x^3$$

Finding the derivative of this function yields

$$f'(x) = 12x^3 + 6x^2$$

The derivative that we have found is referred to as a "first" derivative since we have found the derivative of the function once. Suppose that we take the derivative that we have just found <u>and find the derivative of it</u>. This is known as a "second" derivative. It is written using two prime symbols to alert the reader:

$$f''(x) = 36x^2 + 12x$$

Notice that we have not changed our shortcut of finding the derivative of simple polynomials. We have simply employed it more than one time to the same function.

If we wish, we can find the derivative of the above expression. This is known as a third derivative and it expressed with three prime symbols:

$$f'''(x) = 72x + 12$$

In the last section we learned that it is possible to express derivatives in a different fashion using the language of differentials. How would we express a second or third order derivative using differentials? Suppose that we have the function

$$y = 2x^5 - 7x^2 + 9$$

Expressed using differentials, the first derivative would be:

$$\frac{dy}{dx} = 10x^4 - 14x$$

Now finding the second derivative:

$$\frac{d^2y}{dx^2} = 40x^3 - 14$$

Notice the 2's that appear in the numerator and denominator. **The 2's do not imply that anything is being squared!** This is simply the way that we alert the reader that a second derivative has been calculated.

Finding the third derivative:

$$\frac{d^3y}{dx^3} = 120x^2$$

We can take this as far as we wish (fourth derivatives, fifth derivatives, etc.). Notice that in the case of simple polynomials, like our examples above, we will eventually arrive at zero if we calculate enough derivatives of our function. But what have we found? When we find the second derivative of a function, what is it that we have actually calculated?

Remember that when we find the derivative of something, we are finding the rate at which something is changing. When we find the first derivative of a function, we are finding the rate of change of the dependent variable with respect to the independent variable as well as the slope of the tangent line to the curve.

When we find the second derivative of a function, we are finding an expression for the rate of change of the first derivative. Since the first derivative is the same thing as the tangent line to the curve, we are finding the rate at which the slope of the tangent line is changing at a certain point on the function.

The concept of a higher order derivative and its uses will become much clearer in the next section as we apply it to some physical situations.

Exercises

Find the first and second derivative of the following functions:

Section I
Remember to record your answer as dy/dx, etc.

1.

$$y = 5x^3 + 6x^2$$

2.

$$y = 7x^4 - 8x$$

3.

$$y = 6x^6 - 4x^3 + 3x^2$$

4.

$$y = \sqrt{x}$$

5.

$$y = \frac{4}{x^2}$$

Section II
Remember to record your answers as f'(x) and f''(x)

6.

$$f(x) = 5x^6 - 7x^3 + 9x$$

7.

$$f(x) = 3x^{-4} + 6x^{-3}$$

8.

$$f(x) = \frac{3}{4}x^5 - \sqrt{x}$$

9.

$$f(x) = \sqrt{x+1}$$

10.

$$f(x) = \frac{7}{\sqrt{x}}$$

Section III

In this section, remember to write the derivatives in terms of the dependent variable and independent variables – dB/dt, dP/dr, etc.

11.

$$x = 5t^4 - 8t^3$$

12.

$$F = 7s^3 + 8s - 3$$

13.

$$P = 4w^6 - \frac{2}{3}w^4$$

14.

$$B = \sqrt{t}$$

15.

$$Z = \frac{4}{g^3} + 7g$$

SOLUTIONS

1.

$$\frac{dy}{dx} = 15x^2 + 12x$$

$$\frac{d^2y}{dx^2} = 30x + 12$$

2.

$$\frac{dy}{dx} = 28x^3 - 8$$

$$\frac{d^2y}{dx^2} = 84x^2$$

3.

$$\frac{dy}{dx} = 36x^5 - 12x^2 + 6x$$

$$\frac{d^2y}{dx^2} = 180x^4 - 24x + 6$$

4.   First step is to rewrite the function using a fractional exponent:

$$y = x^{\frac{1}{2}}$$

Now we can find the first and second derivatives of our function:

$$\frac{dy}{dx} = \frac{1}{2}x^{-\frac{1}{2}}$$

$$\frac{d^2y}{dx^2} = -\frac{1}{4}x^{-\frac{3}{2}}$$

5.   First we move the denominator to the numerator:

$$y = 4x^{-2}$$

$$\frac{dy}{dx} = -8x^{-3}$$

$$\frac{d^2y}{dx^2} = 24x^{-4}$$

6.

$$f'(x) = 30x^5 - 21x^2 + 9$$

$$f''(x) = 150x^4 - 42x$$

7.

$$f'(x) = -12x^{-5} - 18x^{-4}$$

$$f''(x) = 60x^{-6} + 72x^{-5}$$

8. First we rewrite our function to remove the radical:

$$f(x) = \frac{3}{4}x^5 - x^{\frac{1}{2}}$$

Now finding the first and second derivative:

$$f'(x) = \frac{15}{4}x^4 - \frac{1}{2}x^{-\frac{1}{2}}$$

$$f''(x) = \frac{60}{4}x^3 + \frac{1}{4}x^{-\frac{3}{2}} = 15x^3 + \frac{1}{4}x^{-\frac{3}{2}}$$

9. Eliminating the radical before we find the derivative:

$$f(x) = (x+1)^{\frac{1}{2}}$$

Now finding the first and second derivative:

$$f'(x) = \frac{1}{2}(x+1)^{-\frac{1}{2}}$$

$$f''(x) = -\frac{1}{4}(x+1)^{-\frac{3}{2}}$$

Note that the product rule was used in this problem. You may be noticing that our answer does not have the last term as did our other product rule examples. This is because when we multiplied by the derivative of what is inside the parentheses, we were multiplying by 1.

10. Rewriting the function:

$$f(x) = 7x^{-\frac{1}{2}}$$

Now finding the first and second derivatives:

$$f'(x) = -\frac{7}{2}x^{-\frac{3}{2}}$$

$$f''(x) = \frac{21}{4}x^{-\frac{5}{2}}$$

11.

$$\frac{dx}{dt} = 20t^3 - 24t^2$$

$$\frac{d^2x}{dt^2} = 60t^2 - 48t$$

12.

$$\frac{dF}{ds} = 21s^2 + 8$$

$$\frac{d^2F}{ds^2} = 42s$$

13.

$$\frac{dP}{dw} = 24w^5 - \frac{8}{3}w^3$$

$$\frac{d^2P}{dw^2} = 120w^4 - 8w^2$$

14. Rewriting the function:

$$B = t^{\frac{1}{2}}$$

Now finding the first and second derivative:

$$\frac{dB}{dt} = \frac{1}{2}t^{-\frac{1}{2}}$$

$$\frac{d^2B}{dt^2} = -\frac{1}{4}t^{-\frac{3}{2}}$$

15. We need to move the denominator of the first term into the numerator before finding the derivative:

$$Z = 4g^{-3} + 7g$$

Calculating the first and second derivative:

$$\frac{dZ}{dg} = -12g^{-4} + 7$$

$$\frac{d^2Z}{dg^2} = 48g^{-5}$$

The Relationship Between Displacement, Velocity, and Acceleration

Suppose that we have a car that is moving and we keep track of the distance that the car travels in a certain amount of time. We can take this information and put it onto a graph. Using fancy mathematical language, we can graph the displacement (we'll give this the variable *s*) of the car as a function of time. Since the location of the car depends upon when we look at it, time is going to be our independent variable and displacement is going to be our dependent variable:

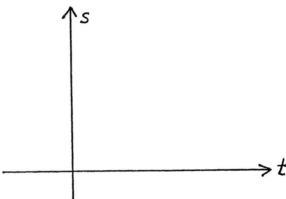

For simplicity, let's assume that the information about the car's location as a function of time forms a straight line:

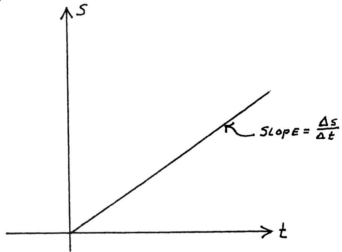

From previous sections, we know how to find the slope of a line. We take the change in the dependent variable and divide it by the change in the independent variable. In our case:

$$slope = \frac{\Delta s}{\Delta t}$$

Now let's think, **physically**, about the above slope. We are discussing the amount of distance traveled in a certain amount of time. <u>This is how we define the speed or velocity of an object!</u>

If we graph the time versus the displacement of an object, the slope of the line will tell us the velocity of the object.

Instead of monitoring the displacement of the car as a function of time, let's monitor the velocity of the car as a function of time. Since the velocity of the car will depend upon when we look at it, time will be our independent variable and velocity will be our dependent variable:

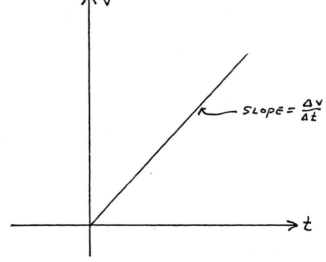

In the above graph we have assumed, for simplicity, that the relationship between time and velocity formed a straight line. If we now find the slope of this line:

$$slope = \frac{\Delta v}{\Delta t}$$

Again, let's interpret, **physically**, what we have found. We have found the change in the velocity in a certain amount of time. This is how we define the acceleration of an object!

If we graph the velocity of versus time for an object, the slope of the line will tell us the acceleration of the object.

In the two situations above, both of our relationships formed straight lines. What if, when we monitored the displacement and velocity of the car, the relationships had not been linear? Suppose that a graph of the displacement versus the time had looked like the following:

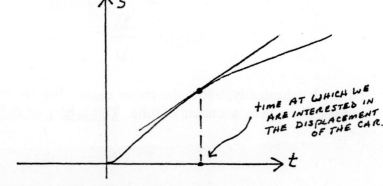

This is where we begin to get the payoff for learning how to find the derivatives of functions. If we draw the tangent line to the curve that is determined by our function, the slope of the tangent line at our point will be the velocity of the car at that instant of time. Remember that finding the slope of the tangent line to the curve is the same thing as finding the derivative of the function.

If we have a function that tells us the displacement of an object as a function of time and we find the derivative of this function, we will have an equation that will tell us the velocity of the object at any time in which we are interested!

Using the language of the last section **velocity is the first derivative of displacement**.

Following this same line of reasoning, suppose that when we monitored the velocity of the car as a function of time, the relationship was not a straight line. Suppose that the relationship was something like the following:

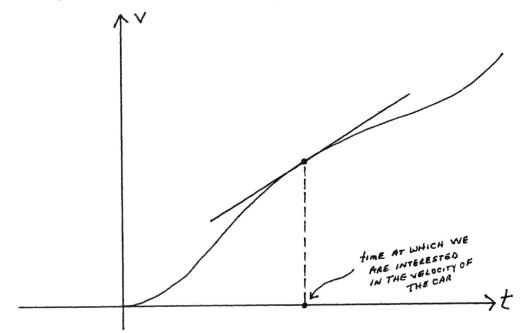

If we again draw a tangent line to the function and find the slope of this tangent line, we will have found the acceleration of the object at that particular instant in time. Finding the slope of this tangent line is the same thing as finding the derivative of the function at that point!

> If we have an expression that tells us the velocity of an object as a function of time, and we find the derivative of this function, we will have found an equation that will tell us the acceleration of the object at any time in which we are interested.

Since acceleration is the derivative of velocity and velocity is the derivative of displacement, this means that acceleration is the second derivative of displacement:

$$v = \frac{ds}{dt}$$

$$a = \frac{dv}{dt} = \frac{d^2s}{dt^2}$$

OK, that's enough theory! Let's take the information from the section above and apply it to an actual example. Suppose that the time-dependent displacement of a certain object is given by

$$s = t^3 + 3t^2 + 5t + 2$$

Let's find, for this object, the displacement, velocity, and acceleration at t = 1 sec.

First off, to find its location, all we have to do is insert 1 sec into our displacement equation everywhere that we see a t:

$$s = 1^3 + 3(1)^2 + 5(1) + 2$$
$$s = 11$$

The object went 11 units (inches, meters, miles, etc. depending upon our problem) during the 1 sec period.

Next, let's find the velocity of the object at t = 1 sec. To find an expression that will yield the velocity of the object at any time in which we are interested, we must find the derivative of the displacement equation:

$$\frac{ds}{dt} = 3t^2 + 6t + 5$$

$$v = 3t^2 + 6t + 5$$

The above equation will give us the velocity of the object at any time. In particular, we are interested in the velocity of the object at 1 sec. To find this, we simply insert 1 sec into our velocity equation:

$$v = 3(1)^2 + 6(1) + 5$$

$$v = 14$$

Again, the units that would be on the velocity would be determined by whatever units we had used to express our displacement.

Lastly, let's find the acceleration of the object. We can do this by finding the derivative of the velocity equation:

$$\frac{dv}{dt} = 6t + 6$$

$$a = 6t + 6$$

Remember that we can also express the acceleration as the second derivative of the displacement:

$$\frac{d^2s}{dt^2} = 6t + 6$$

The above equation will give us the acceleration of the object at any time in which we are interested in it. In particular, we wanted to know the acceleration of the object at t = 1sec. We can find the acceleration by simply inserting 1 sec into our acceleration equation:

$$a = 6(1) + 6$$

$$a = 12$$

And again, the units would depend upon the choice of units for displacement.

In the above example, we see that derivatives and differential calculus have applications in the motion of objects. Are there other areas as well? Yes! How about an application in a completely different area of the physical world? How about an application in electronics?

Suppose that in a certain region of an electric circuit we know the amount of charge as a function of time:

$$q = 5t^4 + 3t$$

(Charge is normally given the variable q and is normally measured in Coulombs)

The derivative of this charge equation is given by:

$$\frac{dq}{dt} = 20t^3 + 3$$

Now we must stop and think about the derivative that we just calculated. We just asked the question: How is the charge in that region changing as time goes along? This is how we define electric current!

> If we have an equation that tells us the amount of electric charge as a function of time, and we find the derivative of this equation, we will have an expression that will tell us the amount of current flow, measured in Amperes, at any time in which we are interested!

In the above example, let's find the current flowing in that region of the circuit at t = 2 sec. Well, we know that the current equation (current is usually given the variable i) is the same as the derivative. This means that for our example:

$$i = 20t^3 + 3$$

To find the current flow at 2 sec, we simply insert 2 into our current equation:

$$i = 20(2)^3 + 3$$
$$i = 163 \, amps$$

At this stage we must note something extremely important. In our two examples, the functions with which we started were simple polynomials.

The relationships between displacement, velocity and acceleration, as well as the relationship between charge and current hold regardless of the types of functions used. In other words, if we had started with an equation for the charge that involved a trigonometric function, the derivative would still give us an equation for the current flow.

Application exercises

This set of exercises is meant to reinforce all of the concepts discussed up until this point as well as illustrate a few of the physical situations to which differential calculus can be applied. The shortcuts that have been covered, the ideas of dependent and independent variables, as well as the concepts of higher order derivatives are to be used in the following exercises.

It was presented that the physical quantities of displacement, velocity, and acceleration are related to one another through the derivative. The velocity of an object is the derivative of the displacement equation for the object and the acceleration equation is the derivative of the velocity equation for the object. This means, again, that the acceleration equation is the 2nd derivative of the displacement equation. Use these facts to solve the following two problems.

1. The location of a certain object (x) is dependent upon the time. If the location of the object is given by:

$$x = 4t^3 + 2t^2$$

    Find:
    a) an equation for the velocity of the object
    b) an equation for the acceleration of the object
    c) the location, velocity, and acceleration of the object at t = 1

2. If the velocity of a certain particle is time-dependent and given by:

$$v = 4t^2 + 5t$$

    find the acceleration of the particle at t = 2.

In the next two problems, we want to focus on the relationship between electric charge and electric current. Use the fact that the current is the first derivative of the electric charge to solve the following two problems. In the following, electric charge is expressed in Coulombs, time is expressed in seconds and current is in Amps.

3. If the amount of electric charge in a certain region of a circuit is given by:

$$q = 2t^3 + 3$$

Find:
a)   an equation for the current flow in that region of the circuit
b)   the charge at t = 3 sec
c)   the current flow at t = 3 sec

4.   If the electric charge in a region is given by:

$$q = \sqrt[3]{t^5} + t$$

find the current flow at t = 1 sec.

The concept of a derivative can also be used to assist us in geometry. It allows us to find the rate at which one geometric quantity changes if we change another geometric quantity.

5.   The volume of a sphere is dependent upon the radius of the sphere and is calculated using:

$$V = \frac{4}{3}\pi r^3$$

a)   Find an expression for the rate of change of the volume with respect to the radius.
b)   Find the rate of change of the volume when the radius is equal to 5 inches.

6.   The area of a circle is found using:

$$A = \pi r^2$$

Find the rate of change of the area with respect to the radius when the radius is equal to 6cm.

The next six exercises are a sampling of other physical situations to which we can apply differential calculus.

7.   The magnetic field (B) in a region is given by:

$$B = 8t^3 - \sqrt{t}$$

If the magnetic field is expressed in Tesla and time in seconds, find the rate of change of the magnetic field at t = 1 sec.

8. The force (F) that is exerted on a particular system is dependent upon the location (x). Find the rate of change of the force with respect to the location at x = 4 if the force is given by:

$$F = 2x^2 + 3x + 5$$

9. In an alternating current circuit, the voltage oscillates from positive to negative in the form of a sine wave. If the voltage source in a particular circuit is given by:

$$V = 6\sin(5t)$$

find an expression for the rate at which the voltage is changing with respect to the time.

10. The rate at which a radioactive substance decays is expressed in terms of its half-life. The half-life for a material, we give this the variable λ, is the amount of time required until one half of the material remains.

The equation that expresses the number of nuclei, N, of the substance that remains after a time, t, is given by:

$$N = N_0 e^{-\lambda t}$$

where N_0 is the initial number of nuclei before the decay began and λ is the half-life of the material. Suppose that a certain material begins with an initial number of nuclei of 10,000 and has a half-life of 5 years.

a) Write the equation that would give the number of remaining nuclei for this substance.

b) Find the expression for the rate of change of the number of nuclei with respect to time.

SOLUTIONS

1. a) $v = 12t^2 + 4t$

    b) $a = 24t + 4$

    c) $x = 6$

          $v = 16$

          $a = 28$

2. First finding the acceleration equation for the system:

    $a = 8t + 5$

    Now inserting our time of interest into the acceleration equation:

    $a = 8(2) + 5 = 21$

3. a) $i = 6t^2$

    b)   Inserting 3 into our charge equation:

          $q = 2(3)^3 + 3 = 57$ Coulombs

    c)   Inserting 3 into our current equation:

          $i = 6(3)^2 = 54$ Amps

4. First finding the current equation from the charge equation:

    $$i = \frac{5}{3}t^{\frac{2}{3}} + 1$$

    Now inserting our time of interest, t = 1 sec:

    $i = 8/3$ Amps

5. a)

    $$\frac{dV}{dr} = 4\pi r^2$$

    b) 100π

6. First finding the equation for the rate of change of the area with respect to the radius:

$$\frac{dA}{dr} = 2\pi r$$

Thus, the rate of change when r = 6cm is 12π cm.

7. The first step is to rewrite the magnetic field as:

$$B = 8t^3 - t^{\frac{1}{2}}$$

Next, we find the equation for the rate of change of the magnetic field with respect to time:

$$\frac{dB}{dt} = 24t^2 - \frac{1}{2}t^{-\frac{1}{2}}$$

Now inserting our time of interest:

$$\frac{dB}{dt} = 24(1)^2 - \frac{1}{2}(1)^{-\frac{1}{2}} = 23.5\frac{Tesla}{sec}$$

8. We first find an expression for the rate of change of the force with respect to x:

$$\frac{dF}{dx} = 4x + 3$$

Now finding the rate of change at our point of interest:

$$\frac{dF}{dx} = 4(4) + 3 = 19$$

9. The rate of change of the voltage with respect to the time is another way of asking us to calculate the derivative:

$$\frac{dV}{dt} = 5(6)\cos(5t) = 30\cos(5t)$$

10. a)

$$N = 10{,}000e^{-5t}$$

   b)

$$\frac{dN}{dt} = (-5)10{,}000e^{-5t} = -50{,}000e^{-5t}$$

11. a)

$$x = .25\cos(4t)$$

   b)

$$\frac{dx}{dt} = -(4)(.25)\sin(4t)$$

12. a)

$$q = .00005\left(1 - e^{-\frac{t}{.005}}\right)$$

   b) If we take the derivative of the charge equation above will give us the current equation:

$$i = \frac{dq}{dt} = (.01)e^{-\frac{t}{.005}}$$

CHAPTER 5

IMPLICIT
DIFFERENTIATION

Implicit Differentiation

This section deals with an interesting area of differential calculus. Implicit differentiation is a method by which we can find the derivatives of functions that are not completely known to us. This method is based on the power rule. Because of this, it would be beneficial to us to do an example to remind ourselves of this shortcut. Note that in the following example, we will be writing our derivatives as dy/dx instead of f '(x).

Example #1

$$y = (4x^2 + 6x + 5)^4$$

$$\frac{dy}{dx} = 4(4x^2 + 6x + 5)^3 (8x + 6)$$

Let's study what we did in this example.

First: We took the exponent on the function, brought it down in front making it a coefficient.

Second: We multiplied by the derivative of what was inside the parentheses.

When we implicitly differentiate, we do the same two steps. The only difference is that the function is not completely written out for us. In other words, the dependent variable is not isolated in the original equation.

Let's look at another equation of this kind. In the following equation:

$$y^3 + 6x^2 = 5x^3$$

we do not have y **explicitly** written down for us in terms of x. Now, in the example above, we could do a little algebra and solve for y:

$$y = \sqrt[3]{5x^3 - 6x^2}$$

Suppose, however, that we have an equation such as:

$$y^3 x^4 + e^{6y} = \cos(x^2)\sin(y^5)$$

Can you imagine trying to reorganize this monster so that y was by itself on one side of the equation?!!

Implicit differentiation gives us a method of finding the derivatives of such expressions without going through the intense algebra required to isolate y.

As we stated above, we are going to use the same two steps in the power rule to find the derivatives of those terms involving y.

Example #2

Let's start with

$$y^5 + 6x^4 = 3x^2$$

We are going to go through and find the derivative of each of the terms. The terms involving x are relatively easily handled since they are simple polynomials. The term involving y^5 is going to require a little more attention.

Remember that y is some function of x. We just do not happen to know what it is! This means that y^5 is a function of x that has been raised to the fifth power and we can, therefore, use the power rule.

Starting with y^5, the first step in the application of the power rule is to take the 5 down, make it a coefficient, and lower the exponent to 4:

$$5y^4$$

The second step in the power rule is to multiply by the derivative of the term that was raised to a power. Unfortunately, we do not know exactly what y is in terms of x. We do know, however, how to write an expression for the derivative of y with respect to x:

$$\frac{dy}{dx}$$

Putting it together, the implicit derivative of y^5 is:

$$5y^4 \frac{dy}{dx}$$

If we put this into our problem, at the same time finding the derivatives of those terms involving x, we have:

$$5y^4 \frac{dy}{dx} + 24x^3 = 6x$$

Our goal is to find the derivative of our unknown function y. We will have it if we can do the algebra required to solve for dy/dx:

$$5y^4 \frac{dy}{dx} + 24x^3 = 6x$$

$$5y^4 \frac{dy}{dx} = 6x - 24x^3$$

$$\frac{dy}{dx} = \frac{6x - 24x^3}{5y^4}$$

We did it! We were able to find the derivative, dy/dx, without ever knowing **explicitly** what y was in terms of x.

OK, we realize that the power rule is really at the heart of the matter for implicit differentiation. Now that we know this, let's write down a step-by-step algorithm for implicit differentiation that's a little easier to follow.

Algorithm for Implicit Differentiation

1) Start on the left side of the equation and find the derivative of each term. Remember that you must also find the derivative of those terms on the right side of the equal sign.
2) Any time that you take the <u>derivative</u> of a y attach a dy/dx.
3) Do the algebra required to isolate dy/dx.

Let's use our implicit differentiation algorithm on a couple of examples.

Example #3

$$y^3 + 6x^2 = e^{7x}$$

First, we start on the left and find the derivative of each term, attaching a dy/dx anytime that we take the derivative of a y:

$$3y^2 \frac{dy}{dx} + 12x = 7e^{7x}$$

Now, we must do the algebra to solve for dy/dx:

$$3y^2 \frac{dy}{dx} = 7e^{7x} - 12x$$

$$\frac{dy}{dx} = \frac{7e^{7x} - 12x}{3y^2}$$

Example #4

$$3x^4 + y^6 + \sin(2x) = y^4$$

Finding the derivative of each term in the equation:

$$12x^3 + 6y^5 \frac{dy}{dx} + 2\cos(2x) = 4y^3 \frac{dy}{dx}$$

This example is a little more difficult because we have dy/dx in more than one term. As a first algebraic step, let's move all the terms that have dy/dx to one side of the equation and move all of the terms that do not have dy/dx to the other side:

$$6y^5 \frac{dy}{dx} - 4y^3 \frac{dy}{dx} = -12x^3 - 2\cos(2x)$$

Since dy/dx is in both terms on the left side, we can factor it out front:

$$\frac{dy}{dx}(6y^5 - 4y^3) = -12x^3 - 2\cos(2x)$$

Finally, dividing by $6y^5 - 4y^3$:

$$\frac{dy}{dx} = \frac{-12x^3 - 2\cos(2x)}{6y^5 - 4y^3}$$

Example #5

$$x^3 y^5 + 6x^2 = \sin(4x)$$

This example is more complex than the previous two because of the first term. Remember that y is actually a function of x. Because of this, we can view the first term as a product of two functions of x. This means that we will be able to find the derivative of the first term using the product rule. The x^3 is the first term and y^5 is the second term. Using the product rule:

> The first times the derivative of the second plus the second times the derivative of the first

yields the derivative of the first term:

$$x^3 (5y^4 \frac{dy}{dx}) + y^5 (3x^2)$$

Notice the dy/dx term that has been attached to the first term. Remember that we are supposed to attach it whenever we find the derivative of a term involving y.

Putting this expression in and finding the derivatives of the other terms in the equation:

$$x^3 (5y^4 \frac{dy}{dx}) + y^5 (3x^2) + 12x = 4\cos(4x)$$

Now solving for dy/dx:

$$x^3 (5y^4 \frac{dy}{dx}) = 4\cos(4x) - 12x - y^5 (3x^2)$$

$$\frac{dy}{dx} = \frac{4\cos(4x) - 12x - y^5 (3x^2)}{x^3 (5y^4)}$$

Exercises

Implicitly differentiate the following expressions:

1.

$$y^2 + 3x^5 = 4x$$

2.

$$3y^4 + \sin(5x) = 7$$

3.

$$5x + \sqrt{y} = e^{8x}$$

4.

$$y^3 + y^2 = 7x^4 - 6x$$

5.

$$4y^6 - 3x^2 = 5y^2 + 9x$$

6.

$$x^2 y^3 + 12x = 15x^2$$

7.

$$\frac{x^5}{y^4} - \sin(4x) = (6x^3 + 5x)^4$$

8.

$$\sqrt{x^3} + y^4 = \cos(6x - 4) + 8y^2$$

9.

$$\frac{6}{y^3} + \sqrt[4]{y^3} = \sqrt{5x - 3}$$

10.

$$\sin(6x^2 - 3x) + 4y^3 = \frac{y^4}{5x^7}$$

SOLUTIONS

1.   Our first step is to find the derivative of every term beginning on the left side of the equation. Remember to attach a dy/dx to every term that is a derivative of a y:

$$2y\frac{dy}{dx} + 15x^4 = 4$$

We now have to solve our equation for dy/dx:

$$2y\frac{dy}{dx} = 4 - 15x^4$$

$$\frac{dy}{dx} = \frac{4 - 15x^4}{2y}$$

2.   Starting on the left side and finding the derivative of each term:

$$12y^3\frac{dy}{dx} + 5\cos(5x) = 0$$

Solving for dy/dx:

$$12y^3\frac{dy}{dx} = -5\cos(5x)$$

$$\frac{dy}{dx} = -\frac{-5\cos(5x)}{12y^3}$$

3.   Our first task is to rewrite the second term using a fractional exponent:

$$5x + y^{\frac{1}{2}} = e^{8x}$$

Now finding the derivative of each of the terms:

$$5 + \frac{1}{2} y^{-\frac{1}{2}} \frac{dy}{dx} = 8e^{8x}$$

Solving for dy/dx:

$$\frac{1}{2} y^{-\frac{1}{2}} \frac{dy}{dx} = 8e^{8x} - 5$$

$$\frac{dy}{dx} = \frac{8e^{8x} - 5}{\frac{1}{2} y^{-\frac{1}{2}}}$$

4.   Taking the derivative of each of the terms beginning on the left side:

$$3y^2 \frac{dy}{dx} + 2y \frac{dy}{dx} = 28x^3 - 6$$

This problem requires a little more algebra than the previous three. First we need to factor the dy/dx off of both of the terms on the left side of the equation:

$$\frac{dy}{dx}(3y^2 + 2y) = 28x^3 - 6$$

Solving for dy/dx:

$$\frac{dy}{dx} = \frac{28x^3 - 6}{3y^2 + 2y}$$

5.   Starting on the left and finding the derivative of each term:

$$24y^5 \frac{dy}{dx} - 6x = 10y \frac{dy}{dx} + 9$$

Remember that our goal is to solve this equation for dy/dx. As a first step, let's isolate all of the terms that have a dy/dx on the left side of the equation:

$$24y^5 \frac{dy}{dx} - 10y \frac{dy}{dx} = 9 + 6x$$

Now that we have all of the terms that possess a dy/dx on one side of the equation, we can factor it out front:

$$\frac{dy}{dx}(24y^5 - 10y) = 9 + 6x$$

Finally, solving for dy/dx:

$$\frac{dy}{dx} = \frac{9 + 6x}{24y^5 - 10y}$$

6.   This problem is more difficult than the previous five because of the first term. Because y is a function of x (although an unknown one), the first term is really a product of two functions of x. Because of this, we need to use the product rule to find its derivative. To use the product rule on this term, x^2 will be the first and y^3 will be the second. Remember that we only attach a dy/dx to a term if we've taken the **derivative** of a y!

Here we go!

$$x^2\left(3y^2\frac{dy}{dx}\right)+y^3(2x)+12=30x$$

Now solving for dy/dx:

$$x^2\left(3y^2\frac{dy}{dx}\right)=30x-y^3(2x)-12$$

$$\frac{dy}{dx}=\frac{30x-y^3(2x)-12}{3x^2y^2}$$

7.   This exercise is meant to reinforce many of the shortcuts that were covered in earlier sections. The first term requires the quotient rule, the second term requires the shortcut for the sine function and the term on the right side of the equation requires the power rule.

Finding the derivative of each term beginning on the left side of the equation:

$$\frac{y^4(5x^4)-x^5(4y^3\frac{dy}{dx})}{y^8}-4\cos(4x)=4(6x^3+5x)^3(18x^2+5)$$

Notice in the above equation that we simplified the denominator and wrote the y^4 squared as y^8.

The algebra required to isolate dy/dx is more extensive in this problem than in the previous ones. Since dy/dx is in the numerator of the fraction, our first step is to multiply all of the terms in the equation by y^8:

$$y^4(5x^4) - x^5(4y^3 \frac{dy}{dx}) - 4y^8 \cos(4x) = 4y^8(6x^3 + 5x)^3(18x^2 + 5)$$

Now leaving only the term that possesses a dy/dx on the left side of the equation:

$$-x^5(4y^3 \frac{dy}{dx}) = 4y^8(6x^3 + 5x)^3(18x^2 + 5) + 4y^8 \cos(4x) - y^4(5x^4)$$

Lastly, dividing to isolate dy/dx:

$$\frac{dy}{dx} = \frac{4y^8(6x^3 + 5x)^3(18x^2 + 5) + 4y^8 \cos(4x) - y^4(5x^4)}{-4x^5 y^3}$$

8.   The first step in this problem is to eliminate the radical in the first term using a fractional exponent:

$$x^{\frac{3}{2}} + y^4 = \cos(6x - 4) + 8y^2$$

Taking the derivative of each of the terms in the equation:

$$\frac{3}{2}x^{\frac{1}{2}} + 4y^3 \frac{dy}{dx} = -6\sin(6x - 4) + 16y\frac{dy}{dx}$$

Now we move all of the terms that possess a dy/dx onto one side of the equation:

$$4y^3 \frac{dy}{dx} - 16y\frac{dy}{dx} = -6\sin(6x - 4) - \frac{3}{2}x^{\frac{1}{2}}$$

Factoring out the dy/dx:

$$\frac{dy}{dx}(4y^3 - 16y) = -6\sin(6x-4) - \frac{3}{2}x^{\frac{1}{2}}$$

Solving for dy/dx:

$$\frac{dy}{dx} = \frac{-6\sin(6x-4) - \frac{3}{2}x^{\frac{1}{2}}}{4y^3 - 16y}$$

9. Before trying to find the derivatives of the various terms, we need to move the denominator of the first term into the numerator and remove the radicals using fractional exponents:

$$6y^{-3} + y^{\frac{3}{4}} = (5x-3)^{\frac{1}{2}}$$

Now taking the derivative of each of the terms:

$$-18y^{-4}\frac{dy}{dx} + \frac{3}{4}y^{-\frac{1}{4}}\frac{dy}{dx} = \frac{1}{2}(5x-3)^{-\frac{1}{2}}(5)$$

Factoring out dy/dx:

$$\frac{dy}{dx}\left(-18y^{-4} + \frac{3}{4}y^{-\frac{1}{4}}\right) = \frac{1}{2}(5x-3)^{-\frac{1}{2}}(5)$$

Solving for dy/dx:

$$\frac{dy}{dx} = \frac{\frac{1}{2}(5x-3)^{-\frac{1}{2}}(5)}{-18y^{-4} + \frac{3}{4}y^{-\frac{1}{4}}}$$

10. Find the derivative of each of the terms, remembering to use the quotient rule on the term on the right side of the equation:

$$(12x-3)\cos(6x^2-3x)+12y^2\frac{dy}{dx}=\frac{5x^7(4y^3\frac{dy}{dx})-y^4(35x^6)}{(5x^7)^2}$$

Because of the dy/dx in the numerator of the right side, we need to multiply every term by a factor of $25x^{14}$ to remove the fraction:

$$25x^{14}(12x-3)\cos(6x^2-3x)+300x^{14}y^2\frac{dy}{dx}=5x^7(4y^3\frac{dy}{dx})-y^4(35x^6)$$

Moving all terms that include dy/dx to the left side of the equation:

$$300x^{14}y^2\frac{dy}{dx}-5x^7(4y^3\frac{dy}{dx})=-y^4(35x^6)-25x^{14}(12x-3)\cos(6x^2-3x)$$

Factoring out the dy/dx and dividing to solve for dy/dx:

$$\frac{dy}{dx}=\frac{-y^4(35x^6)-25x^{14}(12x-3)\cos(6x^2-3x)}{300x^{14}y^2-5x^7(4y^3)}$$

CHAPTER 6

MAXIMA, MINIMA, AND POINTS OF INFLECTION

Maxima, Minima, and Points of Inflection

As we have stated many times now, there are two useful ways for us to think about the derivative of a function. Again, these are:

1) The rate at which the dependent variable is changing with respect to the independent variable.
2) The slope of the tangent line to the function at any point along the function in which we might be interested.

In previous sections, it was the first method that we used as we applied the concept of the derivative to real-world situations. We were interested in how one physical quantity was changing with respect to another physical quantity.

In this section, we are going to use the second interpretation of the derivative. We are going to exploit the idea that the derivative of a function is the slope of the tangent line to the curve, and apply it in the real world.

> In this section we are going to learn how to find the maximum or minimum value that a function achieves by utilizing the slope of the tangent line to the curve

When we addressed the idea of the slope of a line in an earlier section, we dealt with three possibilities:

1) The line sloped upwards as we moved to the right along the x-axis (we call this a positive slope)
2) The line sloped downward as we moved to the right along the x-axis (we called this a negative slope)
3) The line was horizontal (we said that the line had a slope of zero)

It is the 3rd possibility listed above that we need for the material in this section.

Let's start with a generic function:

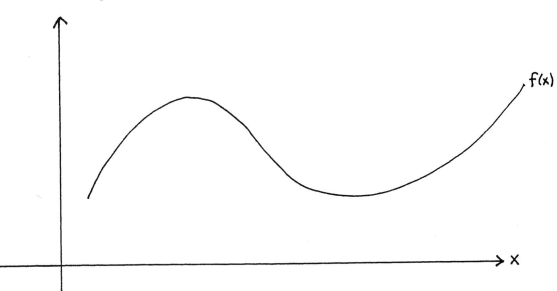

There are an infinite number of points along our function at which we could attach our tangent line. Suppose, however, that we draw the tangent line to the curve at two rather interesting points along our function: x_1, which is at the top of the crest, and x_2, which is at the bottom of the trough:

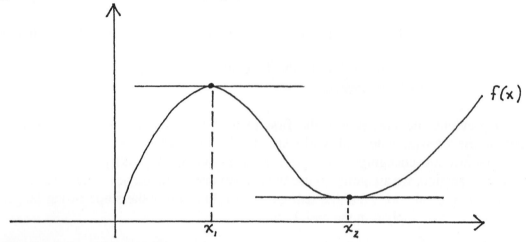

Notice that in each case, the tangent line to the function is horizontal. This, using our 3rd possibility from above, means that the slopes of these lines have a value of zero.

We are now at the heart of the matter:

> The slope of the tangent line to the curve is the derivative of the function. The fact that the slope of the tangent line is equal to zero at these two points means that the derivative of the function is equal to zero at these two points!

We need to pause for a moment and notice something about our two interesting points from the graph above. Notice that the point that we identified as x_1 is the local maximum value that our function achieved along the vertical axis. Also notice that the point that we labeled as x_2 is the local minimum value that the function achieved along the vertical axis.

In other words,

> the points where our functions achieve their local maximum or minimum values have tangent lines that have a slope of zero. This means that at those local maximum or minimum points the derivative of the function must have a value of zero. This is, again, because the slope of the tangent line and the derivative are the same thing

We have just found a very powerful strategy for analyzing our functions. If we can find those points along our function where the derivative has a value of zero, these are the points at which our function is reaching either a local maximum or a local minimum value.

We now find ourselves in the position that we can write down an algorithm for how to identify the local maximum and local minimum values for a function. As we write down this algorithm, please keep in mind that what we are really doing is finding those points along the function that have a tangent line with a slope of zero!

An Algorithm to Find the Local Maximum and/or Local Minimum Values of a Function

1)   Find the derivative of the function
2)   Set the derivative of the function equal to zero
     (Setting the derivative equal to zero is the same thing as asking the question "Where is the derivative equal to zero?")
3)   Algebraically solve for x (or whatever represents the independent variable)
4)   The x's that you have found are the interesting points along your function at which the function is reaching either a local maximum or local minimum value

Let's use our algorithm in a couple of examples.

Example #1

For the function

$$f(x) = \frac{1}{3}x^3 - \frac{1}{2}x^2 - 6x + 5$$

find the points where the function achieves either a local maximum or local minimum value.

The first step in our algorithm is to find the derivative of our function:

$$f'(x) = x^2 - x - 6$$

Next, we are to set the derivative of the function equal to zero:

$$x^2 - x - 6 = 0$$

Again, what we have done in the step above is ask the question "Where is the slope of the tangent line to this curve equal to zero?"

Now, we do the required algebra to solve for x. Notice that the left-hand side of the above equation can be factored:

$$(x-3)(x+2)=0$$

Since the only way that we can have an answer of zero in a multiplication is for one of the factors to be equal to zero. This means that

$$x-3=0$$

or,

$$x+2=0$$

Solving the first one tells us that x = 3 and solving the second one tells us that x = -2.

There are two points along this function at which the function is doing something interesting. The function is reaching a local maximum or minimum value at x = 3 and x = -2.

Example #2

For the function

$$f(x)=3x^2-12x+5$$

find the points along the function where it achieves either a local maximum or local minimum value.

Again using our algorithm, we begin by finding the derivative of the function:

$$f'(x)=6x-12$$

Setting the derivative equal to zero:

$$6x-12=0$$

Executing the appropriate algebra to solve for x tells us that x = 2.

This particular function only has one point at which it is reaching a local maximum or minimum value along the x-axis. This point is x = 2.

By now you might have spotted a slight inadequacy in our algorithm. It finds for us the points at which the function is achieving either a local maximum or local minimum value, but it does not distinguish between the two. So far, we have no way of knowing whether, at our interesting point, the function is reaching a local maximum or a local minimum value.

For us to develop a method to distinguish between maximum or minimum values, we must again return to the concept of the derivative as a rate of change. Since the derivative of our function is the slope of the tangent line:

If we find the derivative of the slope, we have found the rate at which the slope is changing!

Let's look again at the generic function that we used to start this section:

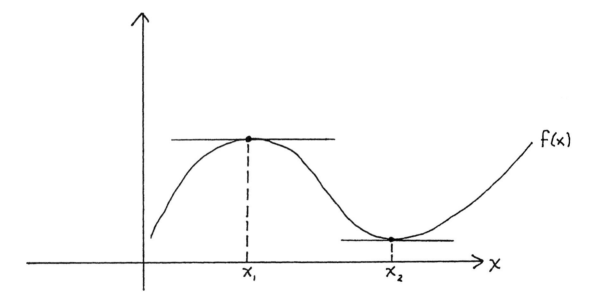

First, we will analyze the tangent line at the point that we labeled x_1:

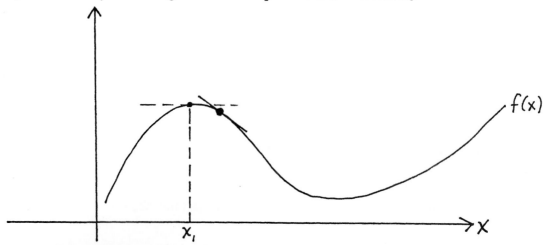

We are going to move to the right on our function and monitor how the slope of our tangent line changes. Notice that as we move to the right along the x-axis, the tangent line goes from being horizontal to sloping downward. This means that as we moved to the right, the slope of our tangent line went from zero to a negative value. Or, in other words:

> At the point x_1, the rate of change of the slope is negative. Since the rate of change of the slope is the same thing as the derivative of the slope, this means that the derivative of the slope at this point is negative.

Next, let's look at the point on our generic function that we labeled as x_2:

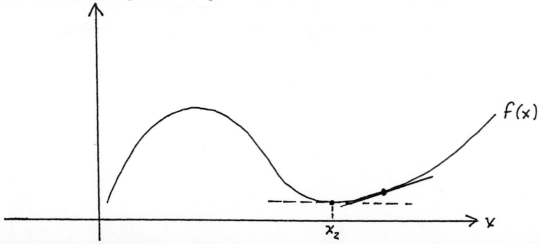

We are again going to move to the right along the x-axis and monitor the response of our tangent line. Notice that as we move to the right, our tangent line goes from horizontal to sloping upward. This means that our tangent, which used to have a slope of zero, now has a positive slope.

Or, in other words,

At the point x_2, the rate of change of the slope is positive. Since the rate of change of the slope is the same thing as the derivative of the slope, this means that at the point x_2, the derivative of the slope is positive.

We have just found a way to distinguish between the maximum and minimum values of our function!

If the derivative of the slope (which is the 2nd derivative of our original function) is negative, we must be at a local maximum. If the derivative of the slope is positive, we must be at a local minimum.

We have one more small point to address and then we are ready to write down our full-blown algorithm and to begin applying it to physical problems. In the statement above, we dealt with the situation where the derivative of the slope was positive, which meant that the second derivative of our original function was greater than zero, and with the situation where the derivative of our slope was negative, which meant that the second derivative of our function was less than zero. We did not, however, address the situation where the derivative of the slope was equal to zero.

There is another possible situation where the tangent line to a curve can be horizontal. In addition to those points along a function that are local maxima or local minima of the function, we can also have a horizontal tangent line at those points where the function changes curvature.

For example, if we look at the function

$$f(x) = x^3$$

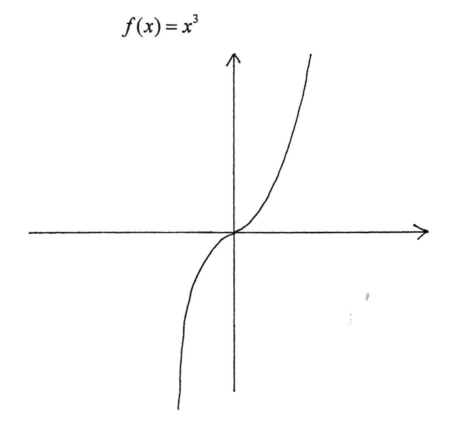

At the point x = 0, the tangent line to the function is zero. Obviously, this point is neither a local maximum nor a local minimum for the function. It is a point on the function where we are changing curvature. This type of point is called a **point of inflection**.

We are finally ready to write out the full algorithm that will find for us, not only the interesting points on a function, but also tell us whether the points are local maxima, local minima, or points of inflection.

Algorithm for finding the maxima, minima, and points of inflection for a function

1) Find the derivative of the function.
2) Set this derivative equal to zero.
   (this step is equivalent to asking the question "Where is the tangent line horizontal?")
3) Solve for *x*. At this point, you have found the interesting points on the function, but have no idea whether they are maxima, minima, or points of inflection.
4) Find the 2nd derivative of the function. Remember that the 2nd derivative is the rate at which the slope of the function is changing.
5) Insert each interesting point into the 2nd derivative.
6) The 2nd derivative now falls into one of three categories:

   a) If the value of the 2nd derivative at the interesting point is positive, a local minimum value for the function is occurring at the interesting point.
   b) If the value of the 2nd derivative at the interesting point is negative, a local maximum for the function is occurring at the interesting point.
   c) If the value of the 2nd derivative at the interesting point is equal to zero, a possible point of inflection is occurring at the point. In this case, points to the left and right of the point of interest must be checked to see if the function is changing concavity at that point.

7) All we have found so far is the place along the x-axis at which the maximum or minimum value is occurring, not the value along the vertical axis itself. To find the actual local maximum or local minimum value that the function is achieving at the interesting point, insert the point into the **original** function.

Well, after an algorithm that long, several examples are definitely in order!

Let's return to our first example in this section. We found the interesting points for the function:

$$f(x) = \frac{1}{3}x^3 - \frac{1}{2}x^2 - 6x + 5$$

Our interesting points turned out to be x = 3 and x = -2. However, when we first approached this function, we did not yet have the ability to identify what was occurring at the points x = 3 and x = -2. We did not know whether the points were maxima, minima, or points of inflection. Let's solve this problem once again, and this time find exactly what is happening at each of our interesting points. We will now use our full algorithm.

First we find the derivative of the function:

$$f'(x) = x^2 - x - 6$$

Next, we set this derivative equal to zero:

$$x^2 - x - 6 = 0$$

Solving this equation for *x* yields x = 3 and x = -2. This is where we left the problem when last we were confronted with it. Now let's finish it using the rest of our algorithm.

We now take the derivative of our slope equation, which is the same thing as taking the 2nd derivative of our original function:

$$f''(x) = 2x - 1$$

The above equation is going to tell us the rate at which the slope of our tangent line is changing.

Next, to find whether our interesting point is a local maximum, a local minimum, or a point of inflection, we simply insert our interesting point into the 2nd derivative and see whether the result is negative, positive, or equal to zero.

Evaluating the second derivative at x = 3:

$$f''(3) = 2(3) - 1 = 5$$

Since the 2nd derivative is positive (5), this means that a local minimum value is occurring at the point x = 3. To find the actual minimum value (how far down the vertical axis the function is reaching), we insert our interesting point back into the original function:

$$f(3) = \frac{1}{3}(3)^3 - \frac{1}{2}(3)^2 - 6(3) + 5$$

$$f(3) = -8.5$$

At the point x = 3, a local minimum value for the function is occurring. The function is achieving a value of 8.5 units down the vertical axis. At no other point near x = 3 will the function go lower than –8.5 units. This is what it means for the function to reach a local minimum value at x = 3.

Now let's insert our other interesting point, x = -2, into the 2nd derivative and see what results:

$$f'(-2) = 2(-2) - 1 = -5$$

Since the 2nd derivative evaluated at our point has produced a result that is negative (-5), this means that a local maximum value for the function is occurring at x = -2. To find the actual maximum value that is being reached at x = -2, we insert –2 into our **original** function:

$$f(-2) = \frac{1}{3}(-2)^3 - \frac{1}{2}(-2)^2 - 6(-2) + 5$$

$$f(-2) = \frac{37}{3} = 12\frac{1}{3}$$

The local maximum value for the function occurs at x = -2. At x = -2, the function achieves a value of 12 1/3 up the vertical axis. At no other point near x = -2 will the function go higher than this. Since there were only two interesting points that fell out once we did the algebra on the first derivative, we are finished. We have found all of the minima, maxima, or points of inflection.

Example #3

Find any/all extreme values of the function

$$f(x) = 5x^2 + 70x - 17$$

First, we find the derivative of the function:

$$f'(x) = 10x + 70$$

Next, we set the derivative equal to zero:

$$10x + 70 = 0$$

Solving for x:

$$x = -7$$

At this point, we do not know what is happening at the point x = -7. All we know is that our function is doing something interesting at this point.

To find out what is actually happening at our interesting point, we must take one more derivative:

$$f''(x) = 10$$

Notice that there is no place in which we can insert our interesting point. **This does not matter!** All that we care about is the sign on the 2nd derivative. In this case, we found that the 2nd derivative had a value of 10, which is positive. This means that the function is achieving a local minimum value at the point x = -7.

If the 2nd derivative has a place in which to insert your interesting point, do so and check the sign. If the 2nd derivative produces a constant number with no place in which to insert your interesting point, just check the sign on the constant number.

So far we know that a local minimum value for the function is occurring at x = -7. Our last step is to find the actual minimum value. We do this, according to our algorithm, by inserting –7 into our **original** function:

$$f(-7) = 5(-7)^2 + 70(-7) - 17 = -262$$

The above example is a bit extreme, but it illustrates the point.

Now that we have investigated the mathematics, it is time to see the applicability of what we have just developed. Using the methods developed in this section, we can now find the maximum or minimum values that a function achieves. This means that through calculus, we will be able to find the maximum or minimum value of the current flow in a particular region of a circuit, the maximum or minimum velocity of a moving object, the maximum or minimum rate of population growth for a culture, etc.

178

Exercises

Find any/all maxima, minima, and points of inflection for the following functions:

1.

$$f(x) = \frac{1}{3}x^3 - \frac{1}{2}x^2 - 12x + 6$$

2.

$$f(x) = x^2$$

3.

$$f(x) = -x^2$$

4.

$$f(x) = x^4$$

5.

$$f(x) = 8x^2 - 1$$

SOLUTIONS

1. First finding the derivative:

$$f'(x) = x^2 - x - 12$$

Setting the derivative equal to zero and solving the x-values:

$$x^2 - x - 12 = 0$$

$$(x-4)(x+3) = 0$$

$$x = 4$$

$$x = -3$$

Now to find out what is happening at our interesting points we find the second derivative:

$$f''(x) = 2x - 1$$

Evaluating the second derivative at x = 4:

$$f''(4) = 2(4) - 1 = 7$$

Since the value of the second derivative at x = 4 is greater than zero, a local minimum is occurring at x = 4. The actual local minimum value is found by inserting x = 4 into the original function:

$$f(4) = \frac{1}{3}(4)^3 - \frac{1}{2}(4)^2 - 12(4) + 6 = -28.667$$

A local minimum value of –28.667 is occurring at x = 4.

Repeating the process for our other point of interest, x = -3:

$$f''(-3) = 2(-3) - 1 = -7$$

Since the second derivative is negative at our point of interest, a local maximum is occurring at x = - 3.

To find the actual local maximum value:

$$f(-3) = \frac{1}{3}(-3)^3 - \frac{1}{2}(-3)^2 - 12(-3) + 6 = 28.5$$

A local maximum value of 28.5 is occurring at x = - 3.

2.   Finding the first derivative, setting it equal to zero and solving for our points of interest:

$$f'(x) = 2x$$
$$2x = 0$$
$$x = 0$$

Now finding the second derivative:

$$f''(x) = 2$$

Notice that the second derivative is a pure number with no place for us to insert our value of x = 0. This does not matter. All we are interested in is the sign of the second derivative. Since 2 is greater than zero, this means that a minimum value of the function is occurring at x = 0. Finding the actual minimum value by inserting x = 0 back into our original function:

$$f(0) = (0)^2 = 0$$

A local minimum value of zero is occurring at x = 0.

3.   Finding the first derivative, setting it equal to zero and solving for x:

$$f'(x) = -2x$$
$$-2x = 0$$
$$x = 0$$

Finding the second derivative and evaluating it:

$$f''(x) = -2$$

Again, there is no place in this problem for us to insert our point of interest. Since the second derivative is negative, this means that a maximum value is occurring at x = 0.

The actual maximum value is:

$$f(0) = -(0)^2 = 0$$

It might seem strange to have a maximum value of zero, but remember that the function $-x^2$ is a parabola that is centered at the origin and opens downward.

4.   Finding the first derivative, setting it equal to zero and solving for x:

$$f'(x) = 4x^3$$
$$4x^3 = 0$$
$$x = 0$$

Calculating the second derivative and evaluating it at our point of interest, x = 0:

$$f''(x) = 12x^2$$
$$f''(0) = 12(0)^2 = 0$$

Since the second derivative is zero, a possible point of inflection is occurring. However, if we graph the function, we see that the concavity is not changing at that point. Therefore, this is not a point of inflection.

5.   Again, finding our first derivative, setting it equal to zero and solving it for x:

$$f'(x) = 16x$$
$$16x = 0$$
$$x = 0$$

Finding the second derivative:

$$f''(x) = 16$$

Since the second derivative is positive, this means that a local minimum value of the function is occurring at our point of interest. The actual minimum value is found by inserting our point of interest, x = 0, into the original function:

$$f(0) = 8(0)^2 - 1 = -1$$

A minimum value of −1 is occurring at x = 0.

CHAPTER 7

INTEGRATION

Integration

As we stated at the beginning of this book, there are two distinct pieces to calculus – differential calculus and integral calculus. Up until this point, we have been learning the various methods and applications of the differential portion of calculus. Now we want to turn our attention to the other half and begin to learn **integral calculus**.

If you remember, when we started our discussion of the derivative of a function, we spent a large amount of time on the concept of a slope. We did this because the concept of a slope is the basic idea behind the derivative. We are going to take a somewhat similar approach as we begin to learn integration.

Just as in the case of the derivative, there is a basic concept behind integration. It is important to keep this in the back of our minds as we learn the mathematical formalism behind integration:

> When we integrate, we are adding something up.

Here we go!

Suppose that we have the following rectangle that has a height of 6 and a width of 4:

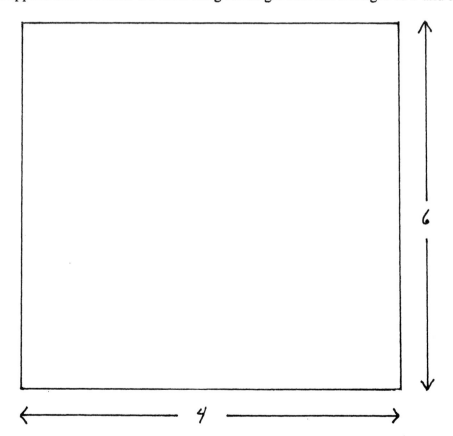

We find that the area of this rectangle, which is found by taking the height times the width, is 24. Let's do something slightly different with the same rectangle that we had above. Let's divide the rectangle into four smaller rectangles, all of which have a width of 1:

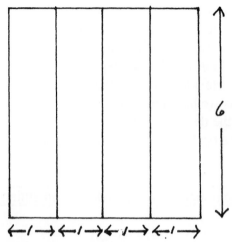

The area of each of the smaller rectangles can be found, again, by taking the height and multiplying by the width. If we do this, we find that each of the smaller rectangles has an area of 6. Notice that we can find the area of our total rectangle by adding up the areas of the four smaller rectangles:

$$\text{Area of large rectangle} = 6 + 6 + 6 + 6 = 24$$

This idea of taking a larger area and breaking it into a sum of smaller areas is extremely important!

If you remember from our discussion on differentiation, there were several ways to think about the derivative:

a) as a rate of change of the dependent variable with respect to the independent variable

b) as the slope of the tangent line to the curve

There are also going to be several different ways that we can think about the integral of a function. Let's use the above concept of areas to develop our first way of thinking about integration. Our discussion of the integral will be broken into two parts:

1) the development of the idea of an integral

2) how to actually calculate the integral of a function

The integral of a function

Suppose that we have the following function, and that we are interested in the area that is under the curve between the points a and b:

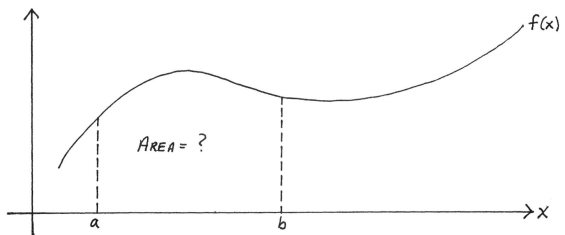

Unfortunately, this is not one of the nice geometric shapes that have simple "plug and chug" equations for us to find the area. We need to develop a technique to find the area under this curve.

The area under the curve between two points is the first way that we want to think about integration.

We do not know how to calculate the area under this curve using a simple equation, such as for a circle, square, etc. We do know, however, how to find the area of a rectangle! Let's take the area that we are interested in and fill it up with a series of **identical width rectangles**. Since the width is along the x-axis, and we are changing our distance as we move along the x-axis the right, let's call the width of each one of our rectangles Δx.

Now that we know how to describe the width of our rectangles, we have to decide their height. Let's start our rectangles out at the x-axis and have them rise up until their left corner touches our curve:

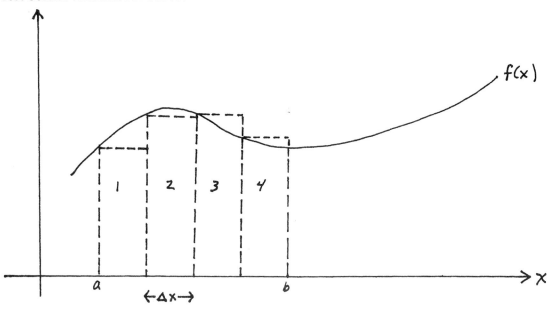

Notice that in the above diagram, the rectangles were numbered one through four. Also notice, and this is important, that each of the rectangles has a height given by f(x) since this is how high each rectangle was allowed to rise.

If we look at rectangle number one, we see that it has a height given by f(x) and a width given by Δx. This means that the area of rectangle number one, which is found by multiplying the height times the width, is f(x)Δx.

We can get an approximation to the area under the curve between the points *a* and *b* by adding together the areas of the four rectangles. Each of the rectangles has a height determined by f(x) and a width given by Δx. The capital Greek letter sigma, Σ, is used to represent a sum. Whenever you see this letter, it means to add up the items that are to the right of it. Using this letter, we can write our sum of the areas of the four rectangles in a nice form.

An approximation to the area under the curve is given by:

$$\sum_{a}^{b} f(x)\Delta x$$

Notice that in the above expression we have the letters *a* and *b* under and above the sigma. This notation means that we are supposed to begin adding up our rectangles at *a* and stop adding them up at the point *b*.

If we now return to our diagram, we see that although our technique involving the areas of the rectangles gave us an approximation to the area under the curve, it was not a very good approximation. Notice that there are regions of area that were not included in any rectangle. Also, there are rectangles that include area that does not actually lie under our curve.

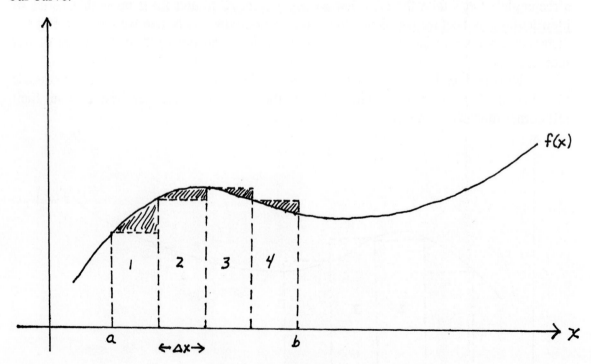

Suppose, though, that instead of inserting four rectangles into the area under the curve, we insert eight. We will use the same technique as before. Each one of our rectangles will have a width that is given by Δx, and a height that is determined by f(x):

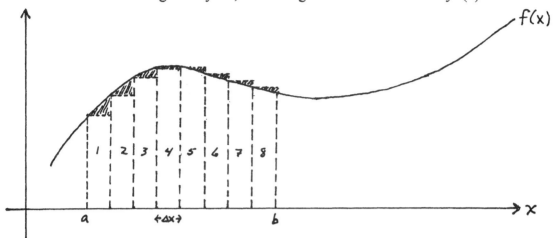

Notice that we have a better approximation to the area under the curve than when we used only four rectangles. We can continue this process as long as we wish. Instead of inserting eight rectangles, we insert sixteen rectangles, each of which has a width given by Δx and a height determined by f(x). Or, how about 32 rectangles! As you can see, the more rectangles that we insert into the area under the curve, the better our approximation becomes. We miss less and less area, and we do not take into account area that we should not. The narrower our rectangles become, the better our approximation to the area becomes.

Suppose that we take a very drastic step. Let's allow our rectangles to become infinitely narrow! Or, using the mathematical language that we developed in our section on derivatives, let's take the limit as Δx goes to zero. If you can picture it, basically, our rectangles look like straight vertical lines. If we allow our rectangles to become infinitely narrow (but not actually zero!) they will sit right on the curve f(x). We will not miss any area, nor will we take any area into account that we should not. We will have the actual area under the curve!

$$Area = \lim_{\Delta x \to 0} \sum_a^b f(x)\Delta x$$

There is a slight notation change that we want to insert at this point. We want to express the width of our infinitely narrow rectangles differently. Up until this point, we have been referring to the width of the rectangles as Δx. Remember that Δ is the Greek letter delta. Let's take the first letter of the word delta, *d*, and express the width of our infinitely narrow rectangles as dx. This will distinguish for us between those rectangles that have a regular thickness versus those rectangles that have an infinitely small thickness.

Using this new notation, we can express the area of one of our infinitely small rectangles as:

$$f(x)dx$$

The fact that our rectangles are infinitely narrow forces us to consider another point. Each time that we reduce the width of our rectangles, we increase the number of them that must be added to include the entire area in which we are interested.

If our rectangles are infinitely narrow, we must add up an infinite number of them in order to calculate the area under the curve.

Just as we changed the notation for the width of the rectangles to remind us that they were infinitely narrow, we want to change our notation for the summation to remind us that we are adding up an infinite number of items. Instead of using the capital Greek letter Σ to represent the sum, we are going to use a Gothic S (the first letter of the word summation). The symbol

$$\int$$

replaces

$$\lim_{\Delta x \to 0} \Sigma$$

keeping the limits a and b. The stretched out S is normally referred to as the **integration symbol**. It reminds us that we are adding up an infinite number of items. Using these two changes in notation, the dx for the width of our rectangles and the integration symbol to represent our sum, we can rewrite our area expression.

$$Area = \lim_{\Delta x \to 0} \sum_{a}^{b} f(x)\Delta x$$

becomes

$$Area = \int_{a}^{b} f(x)dx$$

We have arrived at our first way that we want to think about integration!

The area under a function between two endpoints is called the "integral of the function" between those two endpoints. When we "integrate" the function f(x) between the values *a* and *b*, we are finding the area under the function between them.

Before we move on to how to actually calculate an integral, it is beneficial for us to tear apart the above area equation and look at each piece.

1)   dx is the width of one of our infinitely narrow rectangles

2)   f(x) is the height of each of our infinitely narrow rectangles

3)   f(x)dx is the area of each of our infinitely narrow rectangles

4)   *a* is the point at which we begin to add the areas of our infinitely narrow rectangles. This point, *a*, is also referred to as the "bottom limit of integration"

5)   *b* is the point at which we stop adding the areas of our infinitely narrow rectangles. This point, *b*, is also referred to as the "top limit of integration"

6)   The whole expression

$$\int_{a}^{b} f(x)dx$$

is the total area under the curve between *a* and *b*, found by adding together all of the areas of the infinitely narrow rectangles.

194

How to calculate the integral of a function

In the last section, we found that the integral of a function can be interpreted as the area under the function. In this section, we want to learn the first of many methods that will allow us to actually calculate an integral.

Just as in the case of the derivative, there are some very elaborate and mathematically difficult ways to calculate an integral. In the section on derivatives, we began using a difficult method involving limits, etc., and then moved into the shortcuts. In this section, we are going to move a little faster.

Our goal is to be able to use the ideas of integral calculus to solve physical problems. We are going to take for granted that there exist many mathematically difficult and rigorous ways of calculating integrals and move directly into the shortcuts.

As we begin learning these shortcuts, it is important for us to keep in the backs of our minds that we could be using much more formal techniques to find these integrals. Our first step in learning how to integrate functions involves something called an **antiderivative**.

The antiderivative of a function

At first, the term "antiderivative" appears a little scary. You might be thinking to yourself "I can barely find the derivative of a function and now you want me to find an antiderivative!" Rest assured, the concept of finding an antiderivative is not very difficult.

Suppose that we have an expression such as 2x. If we want to find the antiderivative of 2x, we are looking for the expression that, if we take its derivative, would give us 2x. When we find the antiderivative of an expression, it is basically the reverse of finding the derivative. The function that we would have to have in the first place so that if we found the derivative of it we would get 2x is x^2.

The derivative of x^2 is 2x and the antiderivative of 2x is x^2

Let's try another one. Suppose that we have $3x^2$, and we would like to know its antiderivative. Again, this is another way of asking for the function that, if we take its derivative, will give us $3x^2$. That function is x^3.

The derivative of x^3 is $3x^2$ and the antiderivative of $3x^2$ is x^3

Unknown constants

Now that we have a beginning understanding of the idea of an antiderivative, we need to polish it a little. Suppose that we start with the function:

$$f(x) = x^2 + 3$$

and we find its derivative. The derivative of the above function is 2x.

Suppose that we now have the function:

$$f(x) = x^2 + 12$$

and we calculate its derivative. We, again, have a result of 2x.

What this means is that if we are actually interested in the antiderivative of 2x, there are an infinite number of functions that will work. Actually, x^2 plus any constant will have a derivative of 2x. To allow for the possibility that our original function had a constant that went away when we took the derivative, we add the letter C to the antiderivative. It represents a possible unknown constant.

Example #1

Let's find the antiderivative of 3x + 4. We will attack this problem one piece at a time. First, we need to find the expression that, if we find the derivative of it, will give us 3x. The function that will do that for us is:

$$\frac{3}{2}x^2$$

Notice that if we were to find the derivative of this, we would bring down the exponent of 2, multiply it by 3/2, and lower the exponent by one power. This would give us the 3x that we need.

The next piece is the 4. We need the expression that, if we find the derivative of it, will give us 4. The expression that will do that for us is 4x. This means that our antiderivative thus far is:

$$\frac{3}{2}x^2 + 4x$$

The last step is for us to tack on the letter C at the end to remind us that there might be an unknown constant that goes away in the process of our taking the derivative.

The antiderivative of $3x + 4$ is

$$\frac{3}{2}x^2 + 4x + C$$

Finding the antiderivative of the above expression was not too difficult. We were able to look at each term and reason out what the antiderivative of each term needed to be. What we need, however, is an algorithm for finding the antiderivatives of simple polynomials that will always work even if we are not able to stare at the expression and guess the answer. The following is just such an algorithm.

An algorithm for finding the antiderivative of simple polynomials

When we find the derivative of a simple polynomial, we take the exponent on each term and lower it by one power. This means that the first step in finding the **antiderivative** of a term is to raise the exponent by one power. After we do this, we need to find the correct coefficient that is to be placed in front of the term.

To find the antiderivative of a simple polynomial:
1)   Take the exponent on the term and raise it by one power
2)   Take the NEW exponent on the term, invert it, and multiply in front of the term

Note: It is possible at this stage to write the above algorithm in a little more formal notation. The antiderivative of a general simple polynomial of the form:

$$f(x) = ax^n$$

can be written as

$$\left(\frac{1}{n+1}\right)ax^{n+1}$$

Example #2

As a first example, let's find the antiderivative of x^5. The first step in the algorithm is to raise our current exponent, in this case a 5, by one power:

$$x^6$$

Once we have done this, the second step in our algorithm is to find the correct coefficient to place in front. We are supposed to take our new exponent, in this case a 6, and invert it (flip it). If we invert 6, we get 1/6. This gives us the correct coefficient!

The antiderivative of x^5 is

$$\frac{1}{6}x^6 + C$$

Notice that we added our C, representing our unknown constant.

Example #3

In this example, let's try one that already has a coefficient in front of the term. Let's find the antiderivative of

$$4x^2$$

Our algorithm still works even though there is now a 4 multiplying our expression. Our first step is to take the exponent, in this case a 2, and raise it by one power:

$$x^3$$

Next, we have to find the correct coefficient to place in front of the term. The algorithm tells us to take the NEW exponent and invert it. If we invert 3, we get 1/3. We now take the 1/3 and use it as a coefficient, **remembering to multiply by the 4 that was already in front:**

The antiderivative of $4x^2$ is

$$\frac{1}{3}(4)x^3 + C$$

Of course, in the above expression we could multiply together the 1/3 and the 4 to simplify our expression.

198

Example #4

In this example, let's find the antiderivative of an expression with more than one term. Let's find the antiderivative of

$$2x^5 + 6x^{\frac{2}{3}}$$

We will find the antiderivative of each term separately. First, let's find the antiderivative of $2x^5$. Raising the exponent 5 to 6, inverting the 6 and making it the coefficient gives us the antiderivative of $2x^5$:

$$\frac{1}{6}(2)x^6$$

Next, we need to find the antiderivative of

$$6x^{\frac{2}{3}}$$

Our algorithm tells us to take the existing exponent and add **a whole 1 to it**. In this case, we need to remember that

$$1 = \frac{3}{3}$$

This means that if we add 1 to our exponent, we will have:

$$x^{\frac{5}{3}}$$

If we now flip our new exponent to find the coefficient, remembering to multiply by the 6 that was already in front of the expression, we find the antiderivative of

$$6x^{\frac{2}{3}}$$

is

$$\frac{3}{5}(6)x^{\frac{5}{3}}$$

If we put it all together, the antiderivative of

$$2x^5 + 6x^{\frac{2}{3}}$$

is

$$\frac{1}{6}(2)x^6 + \frac{3}{5}(6)x^{\frac{5}{3}} + C$$

which we can make a little nicer by carrying out the multiplications and reducing the fractions to lowest terms:

$$\frac{1}{3}x^6 + \frac{18}{5}x^{\frac{5}{3}} + C$$

Notice that even though we dealt with the two terms separately, we have only one C in our final answer. The reason for this is the fact that the constants are unknown. If we had written a letter expressing the unknown constant for the first term and also had written a letter expressing the unknown constant for the second term, the terms could be coupled into one unknown constant. In other words, the sum of two unknown constants is still an unknown constant. It is simpler to express it as one unknown constant. Also note that the choice of the letter C to represent the unknown constant is completely arbitrary. We have the flexibility to use any constant symbol that we find convenient.

It is now time to return to the actual topic of this chapter – integration. Now that we know how to find the antiderivative of a function, let's use these antiderivatives to help us calculate our integrals.

Exercises

Find the antiderivative of the following functions. Remember to attach the unknown constant, C, to your final answer.

Section I

1. $f(x) = 2x$

2. $f(x) = 3x^2$

3. $f(x) = 6x + 4$

4. $f(x) = 5x^2 + 7x - 2$

5. $f(x) = 9x^3 - 3x$

Section II

6.
$$f(x) = \sqrt{x}$$

7.
$$f(x) = \frac{3}{x^2}$$

8.
$$f(x) = 8x^2 - \sqrt[3]{x}$$

9.
$$f(x) = \frac{4}{\sqrt{x}}$$

10.
$$f(x) = x^5 - 3x^4 + \sqrt{x}$$

Answers

Section I

1.
$$x^2 + C$$

2.
$$x^3 + C$$

3.
$$3x^2 + 4x + C$$

4.
$$\frac{5}{3}x^3 + \frac{7}{2}x^2 - 2x + C$$

5.
$$\frac{9}{4}x^4 - \frac{3}{2}x^2 + C$$

Section II

6.
$$\frac{2}{3}x^{\frac{3}{2}} + C$$

7.
$$-3x^{-1} + C$$

8.
$$\frac{8}{3}x^3 - \frac{3}{4}x^{\frac{4}{3}} + C$$

9.

$$8x^{\frac{1}{2}} + C$$

10.

$$\frac{1}{6}x^6 - \frac{3}{5}x^5 + \frac{2}{3}x^{\frac{3}{2}} + C$$

Using the antiderivative to calculate an integral

We previously discussed the fact that we could use some very "high powered" mathematics to calculate the integral of a function, just as we did in the case of the derivative. **Instead, we are going to jump directly to the shortcuts.** The antiderivative is going to be our first shortcut in finding the integral of a function.

Let's again refer to our expression for the integral of a function:

$$Area = \int_{a}^{b} f(x)dx$$

The integral of the function f(x) from a to b is the area under the function between the endpoints a and b

Let's deal with a specific function and its area as we develop our first shortcut. Suppose that we have the function x^2, and we would like to know the area under this curve between x = 1 and x = 2:

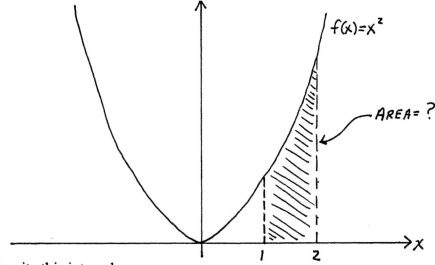

We would write this integral as:

$$\int_{1}^{2} x^2 dx$$

Notice that we have inserted our two endpoints, 1 and 2, in for a and b. We have also inserted our function that is to be integrated as f(x) in our equation.

Let's now use the idea of an antiderivative to calculate this integral, and in turn, the area under this curve between 1 and 2.

The first step in solving the integral is to find the antiderivative of the function x^2. The antiderivative of x^2 is

$$\frac{1}{3}x^3 + C$$

We have not addressed the endpoints of the integral yet. Here is how we write the mathematical sentence:

$$\int_1^2 x^2 dx = \frac{1}{3}x^3 + C \Big|_1^2$$

This statement says that we have found the antiderivative but have not yet dealt with the endpoints of the integral. Notice the straight vertical line that is to the right of the C. This line is always placed after the antiderivative. We place our top endpoint on top of the line and the bottom endpoint on the bottom of the line.

At this stage, you might be asking yourself what happened to the *dx* term in the integral. This is why it is important for us to realize that we have moved directly to the shortcuts. The *dx* term would disappear if we used the extremely formal methods of integration. It is sufficient for our purposes, since we are trying to get to the applications of the integral as quickly as possible, to remember that the *dx* term will go away in the process of finding the antiderivative.

Now we must deal with the endpoints of the integral. We begin by inserting the endpoints into the antiderivative in a very precise way. The endpoints are inserted everywhere that we see the independent variable in the antiderivative.

First, insert the top endpoint into the antiderivative everywhere that you see a variable. The top endpoint is ALWAYS inserted first, regardless of whether it is a positive number, negative number, etc.

Second, insert the bottom endpoint into the antiderivative everywhere that you see a variable. The bottom endpoint is ALWAYS inserted second, regardless of whether it is a positive number, negative number, etc.

Third, subtract the antiderivative with the bottom endpoint inserted from the antiderivative with the top point inserted.

Let's take our sample problem and use the instructions given above to deal with the endpoints of the integral, remembering to insert the top endpoint first and the bottom endpoint second:

$$\int_1^2 x^2 dx = \frac{1}{3}x^3 + C\Big|_1^2 = \left[\frac{1}{3}(2)^3 + C\right] - \left[\frac{1}{3}(1)^3 + C\right]$$

Notice that we inserted the top endpoint of 2 everywhere that we saw an x in the antiderivative. After this, we subtracted. Finally, we inserted the bottom endpoint of 1 everywhere that we saw an x in the antiderivative.

> **Remember, we must subtract off the entire expression with the bottom endpoint inserted.**

Now that we have inserted our endpoints correctly, let's finish doing the arithmetic and find an actual answer to our problem.

The first bracket gives us

$$\frac{8}{3} + C$$

and the second bracket gives us

$$\frac{1}{3} + C$$

which means that our subtraction becomes

$$\left[\frac{8}{3} + C\right] - \left[\frac{1}{3} + C\right]$$

Now let's distribute the negative sign:

$$\frac{8}{3} + C - \frac{1}{3} - C = \frac{7}{3}$$

Our unknown constants cancel!

This is not a coincidence. **<u>Anytime we know the limits of integration (our endpoints) we will always get to a point where the unknown constant disappears</u>.** This is a very good thing if we pause and remember the question that we are trying to solve. We are looking for the area under the curve x^2 between x = 1 and x = 2. We are expecting this answer to have a true numeric value, not to have an unknown constant inside of it!

We finally have our answer:

$$\int_{1}^{2} x^2 \, dx = \frac{7}{3}$$

The area under the curve x^2 between x = 1 and x = 2 is 7/3

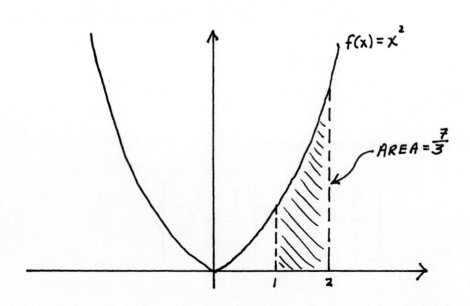

The area of the region that is shaded is an area the same as any other area that you learned how to calculate in geometry. The units for the area will depend upon the units that you used to measure off your two coordinate axes. If you used inches, the area of the shaded region would be in square inches; if you used centimeters, the area would be in square centimeters, etc.

The following is a step-by-step method for calculating the integral of a function.

1)   **Find the antiderivative of the function. Make sure to include the C at the end of the antiderivative to allow for a possible unknown constant.**

2)   **At the end of the antiderivative, draw a straight, vertical line. The top limit of integration is placed at the top of the vertical line and the bottom limit of integration is placed at the bottom of the vertical line. This statement means that you have found the antiderivative, but have not yet dealt with the endpoints.**

3)   **To find a numerical solution, insert the endpoints in the correct order. The top limit of integration (top endpoint) is inserted first and the bottom limit of integration (bottom endpoint) is inserted second.**

4)   **Subtract the expression with the bottom endpoint from the expression with the top endpoint. Make sure to place parentheses or brackets around the expressions. It is imperative that the entire expression be subtracted so that the unknown constant cancels.**

5)   **What you have found is the area under the function that you integrated between your two endpoints.**

Note: Since the constant always cancels, it is acceptable to leave it out of Step#4, but make sure that you include it if you are dealing with a function without definite limits.

Let's do some examples using our recipe.

Example #1

Integrate the function

$$f(x) = x^3$$

between 0 and 1.

(Remember, another way that this problem could have been stated is "find the area under the function x^3 between $x = 0$ and $x = 1$")

First, let's write out the integral that we are trying to solve:

$$\int_0^1 x^3 \, dx$$

Our first step is to find the antiderivative of the function. The antiderivative of x^3 is

$$\frac{1}{4}x^4 + C$$

Now we write down our statement using our vertical line and endpoints:

$$\int_0^1 x^3 \, dx = \frac{1}{4}x^4 + C \Big|_0^1$$

Next, we insert our endpoints, remembering to insert the 1 and then the 0:

$$\frac{1}{4}x^4 + C \Big|_0^1 = \left[\frac{1}{4}(1)^4 + C\right] - \left[\frac{1}{4}(0)^4 + C\right]$$

Notice that each of the terms has a bracket around it. This reminds us that the entire term with the zero inserted is to be subtracted.

Now we do the arithmetic required to find a numerical solution to the problem.

The first bracket gives us:

$$\frac{1}{4} + C$$

and the second bracket gives us:

$$C$$

so that our subtraction problem becomes:

$$\frac{1}{4} + C - C = \frac{1}{4}$$

We have our solution!

$$\int_0^1 x^3 dx = \frac{1}{4}$$

The area under the curve x^3 between $x = 0$ and $x = 1$ is 1/4. Or, as another way of saying it, the integral of the function x^3 between 0 and 1 is 1/4. Again, the units for the area would depend upon the units that we used to set up our coordinate axes.

Example #2

In this example, let's find the integral of a function that has more than one term in it. We will still use the step-by-step recipe to solve the problem.

Integrate

$$f(x) = 2x^2 + 5x$$

between 1 and 3.

First, we set up our integral:

$$\int_1^3 (2x^2 + 5x) dx$$

Next, we find the antiderivative and rewrite our endpoints using our vertical line:

$$\int_{1}^{3}(2x^2+5x)dx = \frac{1}{3}(2)x^3 + \frac{1}{2}(5)x^2 + C\bigg|_{1}^{3}$$

We can make the expression a little easier to deal with by carrying out the multiplications:

$$\int_{1}^{3}(2x^2+5x)dx = \frac{2}{3}x^3 + \frac{5}{2}x^2 + C\bigg|_{1}^{3}$$

Inserting the endpoints:

$$\frac{2}{3}x^3 + \frac{5}{2}x^2 + C\bigg|_{1}^{3} = \left[\frac{2}{3}(3)^3 + \frac{5}{2}(3)^2 + C\right] - \left[\frac{2}{3}(1)^3 + \frac{5}{2}(1)^2 + C\right]$$

Our first bracket yields:

$$\left[18 + 22.5 + C\right] = 40.5 + C$$

and our second bracket yields (rounding to two places):

$$\left[.67 + 2.5 + C\right] = 3.17 + C$$

so that our subtraction problem becomes

$$40.5 + C - 3.17 - C = 37.33$$

We have our solution:

$$\int_{1}^{3}(2x^2+5x)dx = 37.33$$

> If we graphed the function $2x^2 + 5x$, and shaded the region under the curve between $x = 1$ and $x = 3$, it would have an area of 37.33.

Exercises

Integrate the following definite integrals:

1.

$$\int_0^1 x^2 dx$$

2.

$$\int_1^3 (x^2 - 2)dx$$

3.

$$\int_1^5 \frac{1}{2}x dx$$

4.

$$\int_1^2 (3x^2 - x)dx$$

5.

$$\int_0^2 \sqrt{x}dx$$

6.

$$\int_2^4 \frac{5}{x^2}$$

7.

$$\int_{1.5}^{2.3} x^2 dx$$

8.

$$\int_{0}^{.7} (3x-2)dx$$

9.

$$\int_{1}^{3} \frac{\sqrt[3]{x^2}}{4} dx$$

10.

$$\int_{2}^{3} (x+4)dx$$

SOLUTIONS

1.

$$\int_0^1 x^2 dx = \frac{1}{3}x^3 + C\Big|_0^1 = \left[\frac{1}{3}(1)^3 + C\right] - \left[\frac{1}{3}(0)^3 + C\right]$$

$$\int_0^1 x^2 dx = \frac{1}{3}$$

2.

$$\int_1^3 (x^2 - 2)dx = \frac{1}{3}x^3 - 2x + C\Big|_1^3$$

$$= \left[\frac{1}{3}(3)^3 - 2(3) + C\right] - \left[\frac{1}{3}(1)^3 - 2(1) + C\right]$$

$$= 4\frac{2}{3}$$

3.

$$\int_1^5 \frac{1}{2}x\,dx = \frac{1}{4}x^2 + C\Big|_1^5 = \left[\frac{1}{4}(5)^2 + C\right] - \left[\frac{1}{4}(1)^2 + C\right]$$

$$= \frac{24}{4} = 6$$

4.

$$\int\limits_{1}^{2}(3x^2 - x)dx = x^3 - \frac{1}{2}x^2 + C \Big|_{1}^{2}$$

$$= \left[(2)^3 - \frac{1}{2}(2)^2 + C \right] - \left[(1)^3 - \frac{1}{2}(1)^2 + C \right]$$

$$= 5.5$$

5.   The first step to solve this integral is to rewrite the radical using a fractional exponent:

$$\int\limits_{0}^{2}\sqrt{x}\,dx = \int\limits_{0}^{2}x^{\frac{1}{2}}\,dx$$

Now solving our integral:

$$\int\limits_{0}^{2}x^{\frac{1}{2}}\,dx = \frac{2}{3}x^{\frac{3}{2}} + C \Big|_{0}^{2}$$

$$= \left[\frac{2}{3}(2)^{\frac{3}{2}} + C \right] - \left[\frac{2}{3}(0)^{\frac{3}{2}} + C \right]$$

$$= 1.886$$

6. Before trying to integrate this function we need to move the denominator into the numerator:

$$\int_2^4 \frac{5}{x^2}dx = 5x^{-2}$$

Now finding the antiderivative:

$$\int_2^4 5x^{-2}dx = -5x^{-1}+C\Big|_2^4$$

Because we are going to insert the two endpoints to arrive at a numerical solution, it is advantageous for us to rewrite our antiderivative before inserting the endpoints:

$$\int_2^4 5x^{-2}dx = -\frac{5}{x}+C\Big|_2^4$$

$$= \left[-\frac{5}{4}+C\right]-\left[-\frac{5}{2}+C\right]=\frac{5}{4}$$

7.

$$\int_{1.5}^{2.3} x^2 dx = \frac{1}{3}x^3 +C\Big|_{1.5}^{2.3}$$

$$= \left[\frac{1}{3}(2.3)^3+C\right]-\left[\frac{1}{3}(1.5)^3+C\right]=2.93$$

220

8.

$$\int_0^{.7}(3x-2)dx = \frac{3}{2}x^2 - 2x + C\Big|_0^7$$

$$=\left[\frac{3}{2}(.7)^2 - 2(.7) + C\right] - \left[\frac{3}{2}(0)^2 - 2(0) + C\right]$$

$$=-0.665$$

**Although a negative area might seem strange, all that it means is that the area is below the x-axis.

9. This function can be greatly simplified before trying to integrate it:

$$\int_1^3 \frac{\sqrt[3]{x^2}}{4}dx = \int_1^3 \frac{1}{4}x^{\frac{2}{3}}dx$$

$$=\frac{3}{20}x^{\frac{5}{3}} + C\Big|_1^3 = \left[\frac{3}{20}(3)^{\frac{5}{3}} + C\right] - \left[\frac{3}{20}(1)^{\frac{5}{3}} + C\right]$$

$$=.786$$

10.

$$\int_2^3 (x+4)\,dx = \frac{1}{2}x^2 + 4x + C \Big|_2^3$$

$$= \left[\frac{1}{2}(3)^2 + 4(3) + C\right] - \left[\frac{1}{2}(2)^2 + 4(2) + C\right]$$

$$= 6.5$$

222

Definite and Indefinite Integrals

In this section, we want to characterize our integrals. Up until this point, we have always known our limits of integration (our top and bottom endpoints). However, it is possible to find the integral of a function without knowing the limits of integration.

If we know the limits of integration, the integral is called a <u>definite integral</u>. If we do not know the limits of integration, the integral is called an <u>indefinite integral</u>.

Conveniently, there is only one small difference between the method of calculating a definite integral and the method of calculating an indefinite integral.

1) To calculate a definite integral, first find the antiderivative of the function and then insert the endpoints. Remember that the C (the unknown constant) will always cancel when the limits of integration are inserted. The final answer will be a number.

2) To calculate an indefinite integral, simply find the antiderivative of the function and stop at this point. Since we do not know the endpoints, we will not be able to insert them and have the C cancel. <u>The unknown constant, C, always remains in the final answer when calculating an indefinite integral.</u>

Let's use our new terminology to classify the following integrals:

$$\int_1^4 x^5 dx$$

$$\int x^4 dx$$

$$\int_0^7 (x^3 + x^2) dx$$

$$\int (x^5 + 4x^2) dx$$

In the above integrals, the first and the third are definite integrals. The second and the fourth are definite integrals. It does not matter what function is inside the integral. What makes an integral definite or indefinite is purely whether or not we know the limits of integration.

Now that we know how to classify our integrals as definite or indefinite, let's calculate a few.

Example #1

Suppose that we want to calculate the following integral:

$$\int_0^1 x\,dx$$

First, we note that this is a definite integral because we know the limits of integration (in this case 0 and 1). This is the same type of integral that we covered in the last section. Our first step is to find the antiderivative of the function:

$$\int_0^1 x\,dx = \frac{1}{2}x^2 + C \Big|_0^1$$

Inserting the endpoints:

$$\frac{1}{2}x^2 + C \Big|_0^1 = \left[\frac{1}{2}(1)^2 + C\right] - \left[\frac{1}{2}(0)^2 + C\right] = \frac{1}{2}$$

Notice that our final answer is a number and that the unknown constant, C, canceled as we solved the integral.

Example #2

$$\int (3x+4)\,dx$$

First, notice that we do not know the limits of integration for this example. This is an indefinite integral. To calculate this integral, we need to find the antiderivative of the function:

$$\int (3x+4)\,dx = \frac{3}{2}x^2 + 4x + C$$

We're finished! Because we have no endpoints to insert, this is as far as we can go. Notice that the unknown constant, C, remains in our final answer.

224

Basically, the first step in solving any integral, definite or indefinite, is to find the antiderivative of the function. If it is a definite integral, insert the endpoints at this stage. If it is an indefinite integral, we stop after finding the antiderivative, leaving C in our final answer.

Exercises

Integrate the following indefinite integrals
Remember to include the constant of integration, C, in the final answer

1.

$$\int x^2 dx$$

2.

$$\int (x-5)dx$$

3.

$$\int (4x^3 - 5x^2 + 7x)dx$$

4.

$$\int \frac{1}{3}x^4 dx$$

5.

$$\int \sqrt{x}\,dx$$

6.

$$\int \sqrt[4]{x^3}\,dx$$

7.

$$\int (6x^3 + 4x - 9)dx$$

8.

$$\int \left(\frac{x}{4} \right) dx$$

9.

$$\int (5x + \sqrt{x})\, dx$$

10.

$$\int 4\, dx$$

Answers

1.

$$\int x^2 dx = \frac{1}{3}x^3 + C$$

2.

$$\int (x-5)dx = \frac{1}{2}x^2 - 5x + C$$

3.

$$\int (4x^3 - 5x^2 + 7x)dx = x^4 - \frac{5}{3}x^3 + \frac{7}{2}x^2 + C$$

4.

$$\int \frac{1}{3}x^4 dx = \frac{1}{15}x^5 + C$$

5.

$$\int \sqrt{x}dx = \int x^{\frac{1}{2}}dx = \frac{2}{3}x^{\frac{3}{2}} + C$$

6.

$$\int \sqrt[4]{x^3}dx = \int x^{\frac{3}{4}}dx = \frac{4}{7}x^{\frac{7}{4}} + C$$

7.

$$\int (6x^3 + 4x - 9)dx = \frac{3}{2}x^4 + 2x^2 - 9x + C$$

8.

$$\int \frac{x}{4}dx = \int \frac{1}{4}xdx = \frac{1}{8}x^2 + C$$

9.

$$\int (5x + \sqrt{x})dx = \int (5x + x^{\frac{1}{2}})dx = \frac{5}{2}x^2 + \frac{2}{3}x^{\frac{3}{2}} + C$$

10.

$$\int 4dx = 4x + C$$

Exercises

Calculate the following definite and indefinite integrals:

1.

$$\int x^3 dx$$

2.

$$\int_1^2 (x+2)dx$$

3.

$$\int_0^3 x dx$$

4.

$$\int \sqrt{x^3} dx$$

5.

$$\int \frac{5}{x^2} dx$$

6.

$$\int_1^2 (x^3 - x)dx$$

7.

$$\int (\sqrt[3]{x} + x^5)\,dx$$

8.

$$\int_{1.5}^{2.7} (4x + 3)\,dx$$

9.

$$\int \frac{1}{4}\,dx$$

10.

$$\int_{1}^{6} \frac{x}{8}\,dx$$

Answers

1.

$$\frac{1}{4}x^4 + C$$

2.

3.5

3.

4.5

4.

$$\frac{2}{5}x^{\frac{5}{2}} + C$$

5.

$$-\frac{5}{x} + C$$

6.

2.25

7.

$$\frac{3}{4}x^{\frac{4}{3}} + \frac{1}{6}x^6 + C$$

8.

13.68

9.

$$\frac{1}{4}x + C$$

10.

2.1875

A few applications of integration

Before we move on to more elaborate methods of calculating integrals, it is important for us to remember why we are learning this area of mathematics. It is imperative that we keep in the backs of our minds that we are learning calculus so that we can apply it to problems in the real world. Just as in the case of the derivative, there are an unbelievable amount of areas in our world to which we can apply the concepts of integration. Basically, integration can be used any time that the accumulation of one variable is the function of another variable. For example, integration can be used if the total amount of charge depends upon the time that passes, the total amount of work depends upon the distance covered, the total force depends upon the displacement, etc. In this section, we want to discuss one of the above examples.

The work done by a force

This example of an area in which we can apply the concepts of integral calculus is from physics.

If we apply a constant horizontal force to a mass, as in the diagram below, it will move to the right a certain distance. In the diagram, we have called the starting point for the mass x_1 and the stopping point for the mass x_2.

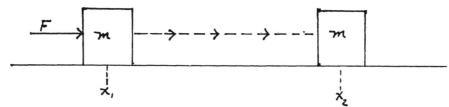

It is possible to define the amount of work done by the force in moving the mass from x_1 to x_2:

> The work done by a constant force in moving a mass is found by taking the force and multiplying it by the distance traveled by the mass.

Let's do an example. In the following, we will use the MKS system of units. This means that our distance will be expressed in meters (m), our force will be expressed in Newtons (N), and our work will be expressed in Joules (J).

Suppose we apply a constant force of 6N to the mass below, and that the mass moves a distance of 5m due to the application of the force:

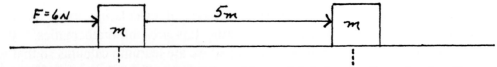

The work done by the force can be found by multiplying the force by the distance:

$$Work = Fd$$

$$Work = (6N)(5m)$$

$$Work = 30J$$

Our constant force did 30 Joules of work in moving the mass a distance of 5 meters

---

In the example above, we were able to find the work done by the force rather easily by multiplying the force by the distance traveled by the mass. Suppose, however, that our force is not a constant. Is it still possible to find the work done by the force even if the force is changing in magnitude at different points along the motion? **YES!**

The work done by a variable force

Suppose the force that is being exerted on the mass depends upon where the mass is located. In a little more formal language, suppose the force is a function of the variable *x*. For example, let's assume the force that is being exerted on our mass is given by the following equation:

$$F(x) = x^2$$

Still operating in the MKS system of units, let's find what the force on the system would be at a couple of different values of *x*.

$$F(1) = 1^2 = 1$$

$\Rightarrow$ There is 1 Newton of force being exerted at x = 1.

$$F(2) = (2)^2 = 4$$

$\Rightarrow$ There are 4 Newtons of force being exerted at x = 2.

Again, the point we are trying to make and understand is that the force being exerted depends upon the location of the mass. To find the force that is being exerted at a certain point, simply insert the value of x into the force equation.

Now that we understand a little bit about variable forces, we want to address the main topic of this section:

How do we use the concepts of integral calculus to find the work done by a non-constant force?

Let's graph our force as a function of the variable x:

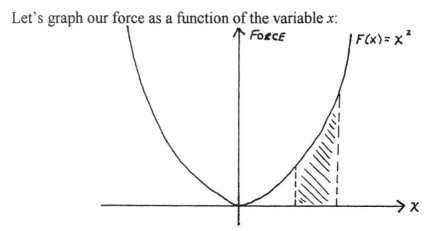

Notice that this is the same graph that we have dealt with in a previous section. Pause for a moment and think about what it would mean to find the area under this function. Using our previous methods, we would fill up the area with infinitely narrow rectangles and then add up these rectangles. Let's analyze one of the infinitely narrow rectangles that would be inside our area.

The height of our infinitely narrow rectangle, as in the previous section, is determined by the function f(x). The width of our infinitely narrow rectangle is dx. To find the area of our rectangle, we multiply the height by the width. Now, attach a physical meaning to the area calculation that was just done.

The height of the rectangle is determined by f(x), which is the force at various distances. The width of the rectangle is dx, an infinitely small piece of distance. By multiplying the two together, we are multiplying a force by a distance!

The area of our infinitely small rectangle is the infinitely small amount of work done by the force in that infinitely small distance.

Since the area of one of our infinitely small rectangles corresponds, physically, to the work done by the force in that infinitely small piece of distance, we can find the total amount of work done by the variable force by adding up all the areas of the infinitely small rectangles. If we are interested in the amount of work done by the force between two physical distances, say x = 1 and x = 4, all we have to do is add up the areas of the rectangles between those two points. But remember what we must do in order to add up the areas of infinitely small rectangles: **we must integrate**.

To find the work done by a variable (non-constant) force between two points, x_1 and x_2, integrate the force function using x_1 and x_2 as the endpoints.

Let's use this technique and finish our example. To find the amount of work done by our force:

$$F(x) = x^2$$

between $x = 1$ and $x = 4$, all we have to do is integrate the function using 1 and 4 as our limits of integration. Writing this in mathematical language:

$$Work = \int_1^4 x^2 dx = \frac{1}{3}x^3 + C \Big|_1^4$$

$$Work = \left[\frac{1}{3}(4)^3 + C\right] - \left[\frac{1}{3}(1)^3 + C\right] = \frac{63}{3} = 21$$

There were 21 Joules of work done by our force between $x = 1$ and $x = 4$

Example

For the variable force given by

$$F(x) = 3x$$

find   a) the force at $x = 2$ and $x = 5$

b) the work done by the non-constant force between $x = 2$ and $x = 5$

---

a)   To find the force exerted at these two points, all we have to do is insert each point into our function.

The force exerted at $x = 2$ is given by:

$$F(2) = 3(2) = 6$$

There are 6 Newtons of force being exerted at x = 2.

The force exerted at x = 5 is given by:

$$F(5) = 3(5) = 15$$

There are 15 Newtons of force being exerted at x = 5.

b) To find the work done by the force between these two points, we integrate the force function using the two points as our limits of integration:

$$Work = \int_{2}^{5} 3x \, dx = \frac{3}{2}x^2 + C \Big|_{2}^{5}$$

$$Work = \left[\frac{3}{2}(5)^2 + C\right] - \left[\frac{3}{2}(2)^2 + C\right]$$

$$Work = \frac{75}{2} - \frac{12}{2} = \frac{63}{2} = 31.5$$

There were 31.5 Joules of work done by the force between x = 2 and x = 5

The Method of Substitution

   Up until this point, we have only dealt with simple polynomials. We were able to integrate the functions by finding the antiderivative of each of the terms separately. In this section, we want to discuss a method of integration that can be used for more difficult functions. This method is known as the method of substitution.

   The method of substitution involves rewriting the integral in a manner that allows us to find the antiderivative simply. It can be used on both definite and indefinite integrals.

> Even though we are learning a different method for finding the integral of a function, we are still finding the area under the function!

   The method of substitution can be used on functions that are similar to the following:

$$\int_{1}^{2} (4x^2 + 3x)^5 (8x + 3)\,dx$$

$$\int (7x^3 - 5x^2)^3 (21x^2 - 10x)\,dx$$

$$\int_{3}^{7} (8x^2 + 6x + 3)^5 (8x + 3)\,dx$$

$$\int (4x^4 - 12x^2)^7 (4x^3 - 6x)\,dx$$

Notice that in the first two examples, we have a term in parentheses that has been raised to a power and the derivative of the expression in the parentheses beside it. In the third example, we again have a term in parentheses raised to a power while the term beside it is one-half of the derivative of the term in parentheses. Lastly, in the fourth example, we have a term in parentheses raised to a power and one-fourth of the derivative of the term in parentheses beside it.

The method of substitution is used when you have an expression raised to a power and something close to the derivative of the expression sitting beside it. The term sitting beside the expression raised to the power must either be the derivative of the term raised to the power or off by a numerical factor.

Our procedure is going to involve rewriting the integral in terms of the variable u. Once we do this, the integral will be in a much simpler form. The actual process of finding the antiderivative takes place while the integral is written in terms of u. At the end of the process, we will substitute our original variable back in, and the result will be the answer to the difficult integral.

Here we go!

As we discuss the method, it will be helpful to apply it to an actual integral. Let's begin with

$$\int (4x^2 + 5x)^6 (8x + 5) dx$$

The first step is to let the letter u be equal to the expression inside the parentheses that has been raised to the power:

$$u = 4x^2 + 5x$$

Next, find the derivative of u with respect to x:

$$\frac{du}{dx} = 8x + 5$$

Remember from our section on differentials, dx is an actual length. Because of this, it is perfectly legal for us to multiply both sides of the above equation by dx:

$$du = (8x + 5)dx$$

Now we are at the stage where it becomes apparent why it is called the method of substitution. We are going to replace each of the terms in our original integral with what they are equal to in terms of the variable u.

First, since we let u be equal to $4x^2 + 5x$, and it has been raised to the sixth power in our integral, this means

$$(4x^2 + 5x)^6 = u^6$$

Next, if we look at du that we calculated above, it is exactly equal to the rest of the terms in our integral:

$$du = (8x + 5)dx$$

Replacing each of the terms in our original integral yields:

$$\int (4x^2 + 5x)^6 (8x + 5)dx = \int u^6 du$$

Notice that what was a difficult integral in terms of the variable x has become a simple integral in terms of the variable u.

The process of finding the antiderivative is carried out now in terms of the variable u!

We solve the indefinite integral that is written in terms of the variable u the same way that we have in previous sections:

$$\int u^6 du = \frac{1}{7}u^7 + C$$

The last step is to reinsert the expression in terms of x. Since $u = 4x^2 + 5x$:

$$\frac{1}{7}u^7 + C = \frac{1}{7}(4x^2 + 5x)^7 + C$$

It's done!

$$\int (4x^2 + 5x)^6 (8x + 5)dx = \frac{1}{7}(4x^2 + 5x)^7 + C$$

We were able to calculate the integral without having to deal with our original function. **It is at this stage that we would insert our endpoints if it was a definite integral.**

As our next example, let's try one in which the exact derivative of the term in parentheses is not in the integral:

$$\int (6x^2 + 8x)^5 (6x + 4)dx$$

The first step remains the same. We set the variable u equal to the term in parentheses that has been raised to the power:

$$u = 6x^2 + 8x$$

Next, as before, we find the derivative of u with respect to x:

$$\frac{du}{dx} = 12x + 8$$

Multiplying both sides by dx:

$$du = (12x + 8)dx$$

Notice that in our original integral, we do not have a factor of $(12x + 8)$dx, but we do have exactly one-half of that, $(6x + 4)$dx. In other words, our term is off by a factor of 2. Since the integral of a function is an actual area under the curve, we cannot simply multiply by 2. This would double the area under the curve.

We can, however, multiply by 2 and ½ at the same time!

Our plan is to multiply by the factor of 2 that we need to make our substitution and to multiply by ½ in front of the integral. Since we are multiplying by both 2 and ½, we have not altered the actual area under the curve.

$$\frac{1}{2} \int (6x^2 + 8x)^5 (2)(6x + 4)dx$$

Distributing the 2:

$$\frac{1}{2} \int (6x^2 + 8x)^5 (12x + 8)dx$$

Notice that the exact derivative of the term raised to the fifth power is sitting beside it! We can now use our method of substitution.

Let

$$u = 6x^2 + 8x$$

Finding the derivative of u with respect to x:

$$\frac{du}{dx} = 12x + 8$$

Multiplying by dx:

$$du = (12x + 8)dx$$

We can now make our substitution remembering the factor of ½ that is in front of the integral:

$$\frac{1}{2} \int (6x^2 + 8x)^5 (12x + 8)dx = \frac{1}{2} \int u^5 du$$

Now carrying out the integration in terms of the variable u:

$$\frac{1}{2} \int u^5 du = \frac{1}{2}\left(\frac{1}{6} u^6 + C \right) = \frac{1}{12} u^6 + C$$

Notice in the above expresssion that when we multiplied the 1/6 by C, we still just wrote C. This is because one-sixth of an unknown constant is still just an unknown constant. Finally, reinserting the fact that u is equal to $6x^2 + 8x$:

$$\frac{1}{12} u^6 + C = \frac{1}{12} (6x^2 + 8x)^6 + C$$

$$\int (6x^2 + 8x)^5 (6x + 4)dx = \frac{1}{12} (6x^2 + 8x)^6 + C$$

As a last example, we want to calculate a definite integral using the method of substitution:

$$\int_0^1 (5x^2 + x)^3 (10x + 1)dx$$

We approach this problem just as before. The only difference will be the insertion of the endpoints at the end of the problem.

First, let

$$u = 5x^2 + x$$

next,

$$\frac{du}{dx} = 10x + 1$$

multiplying by dx:

$$du = (10x + 1)dx$$

We can now rewrite our integral in terms of the variable u:

$$\int (5x^2 + x)^3 (10x + 1)dx = \int u^3 du$$

Notice that we have not included the endpoints of the integration at this stage. It is possible to rewrite the limits of integration for the letter u also, but this will not benefit us in any way. For our purposes, it is simpler to insert the endpoints at the end of the process.

Carrying out the integration in terms of the variable u:

$$\int u^3 du = \frac{1}{4}u^4 + C$$

Reinserting what u was equal to in terms of the variable x:

$$\frac{1}{4}u^4 + C = \frac{1}{4}(5x^2 + x)^4 + C$$

Now that we have found the antiderivative of our function, we are at the stage to insert the endpoints of the integration:

$$\int_{0}^{1}(5x^2 + x)^3(10x + 1)dx = \frac{1}{4}(5x^2 + x)^4 + C\Big|_{0}^{1}$$

$$\frac{1}{4}(5x^2 + x)^4 + C\Big|_{0}^{1} = \left[\frac{1}{4}(5(1)^2 + 1)^4 + C\right] - \left[\frac{1}{4}(5(0)^2 + 1)^4 + C\right]$$

$$\int_{0}^{1}(5x^2 + x)^3(10x + 1)dx = 323.75$$

Exercises

Use the method of substitution to evaluate the following definite and indefinite integrals:

1.

$$\int (3x^2 + 4)^3 6x dx$$

2.

$$\int (6x^3 + 5x + 4)^4 (18x^2 + 5) dx$$

3.

$$\int_0^1 (x^2 + x)^4 (2x + 1) dx$$

4.

$$\int (4x^2 + 6x)^5 (4x + 3) dx$$

5.

$$\int_0^2 (8x^2 + 4x + 3)^3 (4x + 1) dx$$

6.

$$\int (7x^4 - 5x^2)^4 (28x^3 - 10x) dx$$

7.

$$\int_{1}^{3}(2x^3+3x)^4(12x^2+6)dx$$

8.

$$\int(2x^7-8x^3)^5(14x^6-24x^2)dx$$

9.

$$\int_{2}^{3}6(6x-1)^4dx$$

10.

$$\int\frac{(\sqrt{x}+3)^5}{2\sqrt{x}}dx$$

SOLUTIONS

1.

$$u = 3x^2 + 4$$

$$\frac{du}{dx} = 6x$$

$$du = 6xdx$$

Making our substitution:

$$\int (3x^2 + 4)^3 6xdx = \int u^3 du$$

Carrying out the integration in terms of the variable u:

$$\int u^3 du = \frac{1}{4}u^4 + C$$

Reinserting the expression for x:

$$\frac{1}{4}u^4 + C = \frac{1}{4}(3x^2 + 4)^4 + C$$

$$\int (3x^2 + 4)^3 = \frac{1}{4}(3x^2 + 4)^4 + C$$

2.

$$u = 6x^3 + 5x + 4$$

$$\frac{du}{dx} = 18x^2 + 5$$

$$du = (18x^2 + 5)dx$$

Rewriting the integral:

$$\int (6x^3 + 5x + 4)^4 (18x^2 + 5)dx = \int u^4 du$$

Integrating:

$$\int u^4 du = \frac{1}{5}u^5 + C$$

Reinserting x:

$$\frac{1}{5}u^5 + C = \frac{1}{5}(6x^3 + 5x + 4)^5 + C$$

$$\int (6x^3 + 5x + 4)^4 (18x^2 + 5)dx = \frac{1}{5}(6x^3 + 5x + 4)^5 + C$$

3.

$$u = x^2 + x$$

$$\frac{du}{dx} = 2x + 1$$

$$du = (2x + 1)dx$$

Rewriting the integral:

$$\int (x^2 + x)^4 (2x + 1)dx = \int u^4 du$$

Integrating:

$$\int u^4 du = \frac{1}{5}u^5 + C$$

Reinserting x:

$$\frac{1}{5}u^5 + C = \frac{1}{5}(x^2 + x)^5 + C$$

Now dealing with the endpoints:

$$\int_0^1 (x^2 + x)^4 (2x + 1)dx = \frac{1}{5}(x^2 + x)^5 + C \Big|_0^1$$

$$\frac{1}{5}(x^2 + x)^5 + C \Big|_0^1 = \left[\frac{1}{5}(1^2 + 1)^5 + C\right] - \left[\frac{1}{5}(0^2 + 0)^5 + C\right]$$

$$\int_0^1 (x^2 + x)^4 (2x + 1)dx = 6.4$$

4.

$$u = 4x^2 + 6x$$

$$\frac{du}{dx} = 8x + 6$$

$$du = (8x + 6)dx$$

Notice that our du is (8x + 6)dx, but we have (4x+3)dx inside the integral. To change our integral into the form that we need, we must insert a factor of 2 inside the integral and a factor of ½ in front to compensate for it:

$$\int (4x^2 + 6x)^5 (4x + 3)dx = \frac{1}{2} \int (4x^2 + 6x)^5 2(4x + 3)dx$$

Distributing through the 2 will put our integral in the form that we need to make our substitution:

$$\frac{1}{2} \int (4x^2 + 6x)^5 (8x + 6)dx = \frac{1}{2} \int u^5 du$$

Integrating:

$$\frac{1}{2} \int u^5 du = \frac{1}{2} \left[\frac{1}{6} u^6 + C \right] = \frac{1}{12} u^6 + C$$

Reinserting x:

$$\frac{1}{12} u^6 + C = \frac{1}{12} (4x^2 + 6x)^6 + C$$

$$\int (4x^2 + 6x)^5 (4x+3)dx = \frac{1}{12}(4x^2+6x)^6 + C$$

5.

$$u = 8x^2 + 4x + 3$$

$$\frac{du}{dx} = 16x + 4$$

$$du = (16x + 4)dx$$

The term inside the integral, 4x + 1, is ¼ of what we need to make our substitution. We need to multiply it by a factor of 4 and then multiply in front of the integral by ¼ to compensate:

$$\int_0^2 (8x^2 + 4x + 3)^3 (4x+1)dx = \frac{1}{4}\int_0^2 (8x^2 + 4x + 3)^3 4(4x+1)dx$$

$$= \frac{1}{4}\int_0^2 (8x^2 + 4x + 3)^3 (16x+4)dx$$

The integral is now in a form for us to make our substitution:

$$\frac{1}{4}\int (8x^2 + 4x + 3)^3 (16x+4)dx = \frac{1}{4}\int u^3 du$$

Carrying out the integration:

$$\frac{1}{4}\int u^3 du = \frac{1}{4}\left[\frac{1}{4}u^4 + C\right] = \frac{1}{16}u^4 + C$$

Reinserting x:

$$\frac{1}{16}u^4 + C = \frac{1}{16}(8x^2 + 4x + 3)^4 + C$$

Now inserting the limits of integration:

$$\int_0^2 (8x^2 + 4x + 3)^3(4x+1)dx = \frac{1}{16}(8x^2 + 4x + 3)^4 + C \Big|_0^2$$

$$= \left[\frac{1}{16}(8(2)^2 + 4(2) + 3)^4 + C\right] - \left[\frac{1}{16}(8(0)^2 + 4(0) + 3)^4 + C\right]$$

$$= 213670$$

6.

$$u = 7x^4 - 5x^2$$

$$\frac{du}{dx} = 28x^3 - 10x$$

$$du = (28x^3 - 10x)dx$$

Making our substitution:

$$\int (7x^4 - 5x^2)^4 (28x^3 - 10x)dx = \int u^4 du$$

Integrating:

$$\int u^4 du = \frac{1}{5}u^5 + C$$

Reinserting x:

$$\frac{1}{5}u^5 + C = \frac{1}{5}(7x^4 - 5x^2)^5 + C$$

$$\int (7x^4 - 5x^2)^4 (28x^3 - 10x)dx = \frac{1}{5}(7x^4 - 5x^2)^5 + C$$

7.

$$u = 2x^3 + 3x$$

$$\frac{du}{dx} = 6x^2 + 3$$

$$du = (6x^2 + 3)dx$$

If we look at our integral, we see that the term inside is twice our du. We must multiply it by ½ inside the integral and then by 2 in front of the integral to compensate:

$$\int_{1}^{3}(2x^3+3x)^4(12x^2+6)dx = 2\int_{1}^{3}(2x^3+3x)^4\frac{1}{2}(12x^2+6)dx$$

$$= 2\int_{1}^{3}(2x^3+3x)^4(6x^2+3)dx$$

Our integral is now in a form for us to make our substitution:

$$2\int(2x^3+3x)^4(6x^2+3)dx = 2\int u^4 du$$

Integrating:

$$2\int u^4 du = 2\left(\frac{1}{5}u^5+C\right) = \frac{2}{5}u^5+C$$

Reinserting x:

$$\frac{2}{5}u^5+C = \frac{2}{5}(2x^3+3x)^5+C$$

Now inserting our limits of integration:

$$\int_{1}^{3}(2x^3+3x)^4(12x^2+6)dx = \frac{2}{5}(2x^3+3x)^5+C\Big|_{1}^{3}$$

$$= \left[\frac{2}{5}(2(3)^3+3(3))^5+C\right]-\left[\frac{2}{5}(2(1)^3+3(1))^5+C\right]$$

$$= 396973367.2$$

8.

$$u = 2x^7 - 8x^3$$

$$\frac{du}{dx} = 14x^6 - 24x^2$$

$$du = (14x^6 - 24x^2)dx$$

Rewriting the integral in terms of the variable u:

$$\int (2x^7 - 8x^3)^5 (14x^6 - 24x^2)dx = \int u^5 du$$

Integrating:

$$\int u^5 du = \frac{1}{6}u^6 + C$$

Reinserting x:

$$\frac{1}{6}u^6 + C = \frac{1}{6}(2x^7 - 8x^3)^6 + C$$

$$\int (2x^7 - 8x^3)^5 (14x^6 - 24x^2)dx = \frac{1}{6}(2x^7 - 8x^3)^6 + C$$

9. Although this integral looks slightly different, it is still of a form that we can use the method of substitution. Remember that it does not matter in what order we multiply terms. Because of this, we can rewrite our integral before we begin as:

$$\int_{2}^{5}6(6x-1)^{4}\,dx = \int_{2}^{5}(6x-1)^{4}\,6dx$$

Next,

$$u = 6x - 1$$

$$\frac{du}{dx} = 6$$

$$du = 6dx$$

Making our substitution:

$$\int(6x-1)^{4}\,6dx = \int u^{4}\,du$$

Integrating:

$$\int u^{4}\,du = \frac{1}{5}u^{5} + C$$

Reinserting x:

$$\frac{1}{5}u^{5} + C = \frac{1}{5}(6x-1)^{5} + C$$

Evaluating the integral at the limits of integration:

$$\int_{2}^{3} 6(6x-1)^4 dx = \frac{1}{5}(6x-1)^5 + C \Big|_{2}^{3}$$

$$= \left[\frac{1}{5}(6(3)-1)^5 + C\right] - \left[\frac{1}{5}(6(2)-1)^5 + C\right]$$

$$= 251761.2$$

10. The key to this problem is the fractional exponents that we have used so many times before. We can rewrite our integral before we begin the method of substitution as:

$$\int \frac{(\sqrt{x}+3)^5}{2\sqrt{x}} dx = \int \left(x^{\frac{1}{2}}+3\right)^5 \frac{1}{2} x^{-\frac{1}{2}} dx$$

Now, we proceed as usual:

$$u = x^{\frac{1}{2}} + 3$$

$$\frac{du}{dx} = \frac{1}{2} x^{-\frac{1}{2}}$$

$$du = \frac{1}{2} x^{-\frac{1}{2}} dx$$

Making our substitution:

$$\int \left(x^{\frac{1}{2}} + 3 \right)^5 \frac{1}{2} x^{-\frac{1}{2}} dx = \int u^5 du$$

Integrating:

$$\int u^5 du = \frac{1}{6} u^6 + C$$

Reinserting x:

$$\frac{1}{6} u^6 + C = \frac{1}{6} (x^{\frac{1}{2}} + 3)^6 + C$$

$$\int \frac{(\sqrt{x} + 3)^5}{2\sqrt{x}} dx = \frac{1}{6} (\sqrt{x} + 3)^6 + C$$

Exercises

This set of exercises is a mixture of the different types of integrals that have been covered. They cover definite and indefinite integrals as well as simple polynomials and the method of substitution. It is important for the student to be able to identify and solve the different types of integrals.

Solve the following integrals:

1.

$$\int x^3 dx$$

2.

$$\int (5x^2 - 6x + 8)^6 (10x - 6) dx$$

3.

$$\int_1^4 (6x + 7) dx$$

4.

$$\int \frac{4}{x^3} dx$$

5. Round answer to the nearest hundredth

$$\int_1^5 \sqrt{x} \, dx$$

6. Round answer to the nearest hundredth

$$\int_0^3 (\sqrt{x} + 7x + 2) dx$$

7.

$$\int (6x^3 - 4x^2)^5 (9x^2 - 4x)\,dx$$

8.

$$\int_1^{2.6} \frac{x}{3}\,dx$$

9.

$$\int \frac{\sqrt[3]{x}}{5}\,dx$$

10.

$$\int_1^3 (6x - 4)^3\, 6\,dx$$

Answers

1.

$$\frac{1}{4}x^4 + C$$

2.

$$\frac{1}{7}(5x^2 - 6x + 8)^7 + C$$

3.

66

4.

$$-2x^{-2} + C$$

5.

6.79

6.

40.96

7.

$$\frac{1}{12}(6x^3 - 4x^2)^6 + C$$

8.

0.96

9.

$$\frac{3}{20}x^{\frac{4}{3}} + C$$

10.

9600

INDEX